ALGEBRA 1
Tests/Quizzes

D1370163

A Beka Book® Pensacola, FL 32523-9100
an affiliate of PENSACOLA CHRISTIAN COLLEGE®

Teaching Materials

For the Student

Algebra 1

Tests and Quizzes

For the Teacher

Algebra 1 Teacher Edition

Solution Key for *Algebra 1*

Teacher Tests/Quizzes Key

Algebra 1 **Tests/Quizzes**
Second Edition

Editor: G. Parker

To the Teacher

Quizzes

Before Quiz
1. Have the students clear their desks and take out one clean sheet of paper (cover sheet) and a pencil.

2. Distribute the quizzes.

3. Have the students place their cover sheet at the top of the quiz and move it down to cover their answers as they take the quiz.

After Quiz
4. When they have finished, have the students put their pencil away and take out a pen for grading.

5. Have the students exchange papers according to your instructions. Vary the method of exchange from quiz to quiz (pass them forward one seat, back one seat, across the aisle, etc.). Instruct the students to sign their name at the bottom of the paper they grade.

Grading Quiz
6. Give instructions for grading: how many points to deduct for each wrong answer, how to mark the quiz paper, where to write the final score, etc. (Having them grade in a uniform manner saves you time later.)

7. Read the correct answers one time. Tell the students to mark any questions they have with a question mark both by the number in question and by the grade at the top of the paper.

8. Have the students figure the final grade for the paper they are checking by subtracting the total number of points missed from 100. For example, if each answer is worth 8 points and a student misses 2 questions, he would receive an 84 (16 points subtracted from 100).

9. Have the students return the graded paper to the owner. The students should check their own paper briefly, put a question mark by any questions they have, and then pass their paper to the front of the classroom.

After Class
10. Go through the quizzes later, checking the answers, writing the final grades in ink on the quiz papers, and recording the final grades.

Tests

Giving Tests
1. Have the students clear their desks and take out one clean sheet of paper (cover sheet) and a pencil.

2. Distribute the tests.

3. Students should place their cover sheet at the top of the test and move it down to cover their work and answers as they take the test.

4. As students finish, they should bring their test to you and return to their seat. Instruct them to quietly study a subject other than algebra while they wait for their classmates to finish.

5. Always grade tests yourself, although you may wish to have a reliable student alphabetize the tests for you to make recording grades easier.

6. Wait until after you have gone over the graded tests in class before recording the grades in your grade book.

Going Over Tests

1. Have the students clear their desks and take out a pen.

2. Distribute the graded tests.

3. To go over the test, ask if a student in the class has all of the answers in the first section correct. Choose such a student to read the questions and answers. Continue this procedure until all of the answers on the test have been given.

4. If students find that a question has been graded incorrectly, they should write the number of the incorrectly graded question at the top of the first page with a question mark. Check these questions after class before you record the grades.

Averaging Grades

Average a nine-weeks grade in the following way:

1/3 Quiz average	93
1/3 Test average	$88 + 96 \div 2 = 92$
1/3 Nine-weeks exam or semester exam	$\underline{+ 94}$
	$279 \div 3 = 93$ *(nine-weeks grade)*

Average a semester grade in the following way:

First nine-weeks average	93
Second nine-weeks average	$\underline{+ 95}$
	$188 \div 2 = 94$ *(semester grade)*

Name _____ Date _____ Score _____

QUIZ 1 *Algebra 1*

Sections 1.1–1.5
(−8 each)

Answer the questions.

_____35_____   **1.** If x equals 5, what is the value of $6x + 2x - x$?

_____6_____   **2.** If x equals 8, what is the value of $\frac{3x}{4}$?

Write an algebraic statement for the following.

_____$x + 5 = 13$_____   **3.** If 5 is added to a number the result is 13.

_____$2x + 1 = 21$_____   **4.** Two times a number plus 1 is 21.

_____$3x - 2 = 25$_____   **5.** Three times a number minus two equals 25.

Solve for *x* by inspection.

_____$x = 4$_____   **6.** $5x = 20$

_____$x = 16$_____   **7.** $\frac{x}{2} = 8$

_____$x = 20$_____   **8.** $x - 5 = 15$

_____$x = 15$_____   **9.** $\frac{2}{3}x = 10$

_____$x = 3$_____   **10.** $x + 4 = 7$

QUIZ 2   *Algebra 1*

Sections 1.6–1.8
(–8 each)

Solve the equation for *x*.

_____ $x = 1$ _____   **1.** $8x - \frac{1}{4} = 7\frac{3}{4}$

_____ $x = 1$ _____   **2.** $3x + 7 - 2 = 8$

_____ $x = 6$ _____   **3.** $5x - 11 = 19$

_____ $x = 30$ _____   **4.** $\frac{5}{6}x = 25$

_____ $x = 4$ _____   **5.** $3x = 12$

_____ $x = 7$ _____   **6.** $x - 2 = 5$

Write an algebraic statement to represent the following.

_____ $500 - y$ _____   **7.** A man gave \$500 to his two sons. He gave *y* dollars to one. Express the amount he gave to the other.

_____ $2n;\ 2n - 4$ _____   **8.** Mary is *n* years old. If John is twice as old, what is his age now? What was his age 4 years ago?

_____ $n + m - p$ _____   **9.** A boy has *n* baseball bats and buys *m* bats more. He then gives away *p* bats. How many does he have left?

Write the equation and solution.

_____ $x + 4x = 70;\ 14,\ 56$ _____   **10.** The sum of two numbers is 70. One number is 4 times the other number. What are the two numbers?

$$
\begin{array}{lll}
x = \text{1st number} & 14 & x + 4x = 70 \\
4x = \text{2nd number} & 56 & 5x = 70 \\
& & x = 14
\end{array}
$$

QUIZ 3   *Algebra 1*

Sections 2.1–2.2
(–8 each)

Write the number of terms.

_____2_____   **1.** $4x - 2y$

_____1_____   **2.** $\frac{3xy^2}{7x}$

_____4_____   **3.** $a + 2b - 3c + 5$

_____2_____   **4.** $5 + b$

Identify each of the following as a monomial, binomial, or trinomial.

_____monomial_____   **5.** $5x$

_____trinomial_____   **6.** $2x + 3y - 6$

_____binomial_____   **7.** $2abc + 32xy$

_____monomial_____   **8.** $\frac{12a}{7x}$

_____binomial_____   **9.** $a + 2b$

Solve the word problem.

_____42_____   **10.** What number increased by $\frac{1}{2}$ of itself equals 63?

$x = \text{number}$

$$x + \frac{x}{2} = 63$$

$$1\frac{1}{2}x = 63$$

$$\frac{2}{3} \cdot \frac{3}{2}x = 63 \cdot \frac{2}{3}$$

$$x = 42$$

Name _____ Date _____ Score _____

QUIZ 4 *Algebra 1*

Represent algebraically.

_____ $x - 10$ _____ **1.** Tom is x years old. Represent his age 10 years ago.

_____ $\frac{8ab}{4c^7}$ or $8ab \div 4c^7$ _____ **2.** Eight times the product of a and b, divided by four times the seventh power of c

_____ xy _____ **3.** The cost of x yards of material at y dollars per yard.

Unite terms.

_____ $9x$ _____ **4.** $3x + 6x$

_____ $9a + b$ _____ **5.** $5a + 2b - b + 4a$

_____ $6x$ _____ **6.** $5x - 3x + 4x$

_____ $5a + 3b + 2c$ _____ **7.** $3a + 4b - a + 2c - b + 3a$

Find the value when *a* = 5 and *b* = 3.

_____ 100 _____ **8.** $(2a)^2$

_____ 1 _____ **9.** $2a - 3b$

_____ 50 _____ **10.** $2a^2$

Name _____ Date _____ Score _____

TEST 1

Algebra 1

Units 1–2

DIRECTIONS: Show all of your work neatly in pencil in the space provided. Copy your answers from your work space into the space provided for the answer. Use another sheet to keep all work and answers covered at all times.

Use mathematical symbols to write the following. *(–4 each)*

$a - 3$ _____ **1.** a decreased by 3

$5n$ _____ **2.** The product of 5 and n

$\frac{3}{4}x = 12$ _____ **3.** $\frac{3}{4}$ of a number is 12.

$3x - 1 = 20$ _____ **4.** Three times a number less 1 is 20.

$5x + 4 = 39$ _____ **5.** Five times a number plus 4 is 39.

$5x - 3 = 32$ _____ **6.** Three less than 5 times a number is 32.

$\frac{4x}{3} = 12$ _____ **7.** Four times a number divided by 3 is 12.

$14 + b$ _____ **8.** John is 14 years old. How old will he be in b years?

Solve the following equations. *(–4 each)*

5 _____ **9.** $3x = 15$

2 _____ **10.** $6a + 2a - 1 = 15$

6 _____ **11.** $\frac{x}{2} = 3$

9 _____ **12.** $x - 3 = 6$

2 _____ **13.** $1.5n = 3.0$

10 _____ **14.** $2m + 5 = 25$

4 _____ **15.** $2\frac{1}{2}x = 10$

1 _____ **16.** $3n + 7 - 2 = 8$

Combine the following terms. *(−4 each)*

4a	**17.** $3a + 2a - a$
4c	**18.** $2b + 3c - b - b + c$
8x + y	**19.** $3x + 2y + 5x - y$

Follow the directions. *(−2 each)*

40	**20.** Find the value of $4ab$ if $a = 5$ and $b = 2$.
6	**21.** Find the value of $\frac{xy}{z}$ if $x = 3$, $y = 4$, and $z = 2$.
30	**22.** Find the value of $3ab - bc$ if $a = 4$, $b = 3$, and $c = 2$.

Write an equation for the following problems and solve. *(−1 each part)*

$3x + x = 32$	**23.** One number is three times another number and their
8, 24	sum is 32. Find the numbers.

$2x - \frac{1}{3}x = 15$	**24.** Twice a number less $\frac{1}{3}$ of the number equals 15. Find the
9	number.

$x + 2x + 4x = 98$	**25.** Divide 98 into three parts such that the second part is
14, 28, 56	twice the first, and the third part is twice the second.

QUIZ 5 _____ *Algebra 1*

Sections 2.7–2.8
(–8 each)

Find the value of each.

_____15_____ **1.** $5 \cdot (10 - 7)$

_____9_____ **2.** $\frac{(6 + 2 \cdot 8 - 4)}{2}$

_____18_____ **3.** $6 + 2 \cdot \left(8 - \frac{4}{2}\right)$

Find the value when $x = 2$, $y = 3$, and $z = 4$.

_____72_____ **4.** $3xyz$

_____81_____ **5.** $(3y)^2$

_____27_____ **6.** $3y^2$

Express in abbreviated form by using exponents.

_____$3a^3x^3y$_____ **7.** $3aaaxxxy$

_____$2x^6$_____ **8.** $2xxxxxx$

Represent algebraically.

_____$3x - 2y^5$_____ **9.** Three times x, minus twice the fifth power of y.

_____$5x + 3y^2$_____ **10.** The sum of five times x and three times the square of y.

Name _____ Date _____ Score _____

QUIZ 6   *Algebra 1*

Sections 3.3–3.6
(–12 each)

Answer the questions.

    circle graph   **1.** What type of graph shows the relation of all the parts to each other and to the whole?

    bar graph   **2.** What type of graph is used to picture data without any connected sequence?

    curved line graph   **3.** What type of graph is used when the data represents gradual or continuous changes?

Draw a line graph to illustrate these statistics. Use graph paper.

4. The temperatures for the week of September 9–15 were the following degrees for the respective days: 90°, 95°, 93°, 94°, 99°, 97°, and 100°.

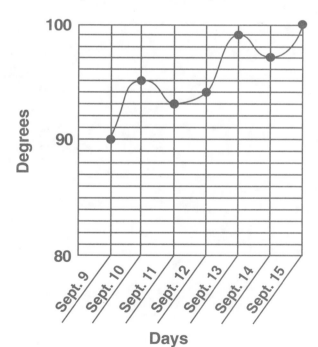

Temperatures for September 9–15

Solve the word problem.

    10   **5.** The sum of a certain number and 3 times the number is 40. What is the number?

$$x = \text{number}$$
$$x + 3x = 40$$
$$4x = 40$$
$$x = 10$$

QUIZ 7   *Algebra 1*

Sections 4.1–4.7
(–8 each)

Give the amount earned for the given hours if the pay for two hours is $10.80.

_____ $27.00 _____   **1.** 5 hours

_____ $21.60 _____   **2.** 4 hours

Find each amount.

_____ $120 _____   **3.** $i = prt$ Find i if $p = \$500$, $r = 6\%$, and $t = 4$ years.

_____ 51.84 in.^{2} _____   **4.** $A = s^2$ Find A when $s = 7.2$ inches.

_____ 105 ft.^{3} _____   **5.** $V = lwh$ Find V when $l = 7$ feet, $w = 5$ feet, and $h = 3$ feet.

_____ 50.24 yd.^{2} _____   **6.** $A = \pi r^2$ Find A when $\pi = 3.14$ and $r = 4$ yards.

Identify the circled part as a *constant, independent variable*, or *dependent variable*.

_____ independent variable _____   **7.** $V = lw\boxed{h}$

_____ constant _____   **8.** $P = \boxed{4}s$

_____ dependent variable _____   **9.** $\boxed{A} = \pi r^2$

_____ independent variable _____   **10.** $i = p\boxed{r}t$

     15

QUIZ 8

Sections 4.8–4.12
(–8 each)

Find each amount.

$F = 140°$

1. $F = \frac{9}{5}C + 32°$ Find F if $C = 60°$.

$C = 10°$

2. $C = \frac{5}{9}(F - 32°)$ Find C if $F = 50°$.

$r = 16$ mph

3. $r = \frac{d}{t}$ Find r if $d = 80$ miles and $t = 5$ hours.

1,680 cu. ft.

4. $V = lwh$ Find V if $l = 12$ ft., $w = 10$ ft., $h = 14$ ft.

Solve for the indicated variable.

$w = \frac{V}{lh}$

5. $V = lwh$ Solve the formula for w.

$b = \frac{2A}{h}$

6. $A = \frac{1}{2}bh$ Solve the formula for b.

Identify the number of significant figures in each answer. Do not work the problem.

2

7. 29×1.12

1

8. 5×8

3

9. 3.25×6.02

1

10. 7.2×4

Name _____ Date _____ Score _____

QUIZ 9 _____ *Algebra 1*

Find each amount. Disregard significant figures.

_____15 in.²_____ **1.** $A = bh$ Find A when $b = 3$ inches and $h = 5$ inches.

_____10 ft.²_____ **2.** $A = \frac{1}{2}bh$ Find A when $b = 4$ feet and $h = 5$ feet.

_____163.28 ft._____ **3.** $c = \pi d$ Find c when $\pi = 3.14$ and $d = 52$ feet.

_____1,452 in.³_____ **4.** $V = lwh$ Find V when $l = 12$ inches, $w = 11$ inches, and $h = 11$ inches.

_____24 ft.²_____ **5.** $A = 6e^2$ Find A when $e = 2$ feet.

Solve for the indicated variable.

_____$b = \frac{A}{h}$_____ **6.** $A = bh$ Solve for b.

_____$h = \frac{2A}{b}$_____ **7.** $A = \frac{1}{2}bh$ Solve for h.

_____$d = \frac{c}{\pi}$_____ **8.** $c = \pi d$ Solve for d.

_____$h = \frac{V}{lw}$_____ **9.** $V = lwh$ Solve for h.

_____$h = \frac{A}{2\pi r}$_____ **10.** $A = 2\pi rh$ Solve for h.

TEST 2 _____ *Algebra 1*

Units 2–4

DIRECTIONS: Show all of your work neatly in pencil in the space provided. Copy your answers from your work space into the space provided for the answer. Use another sheet to keep all work and answers covered at all times.

TRUE-FALSE: If the statement is always true, write *true* in the space; if the statement is *not* always true, write *false* in the space. *(–3 each)*

_____ False _____   **1.** The expression $2x^2 + 4x - 7$ is a binomial.

_____ False _____   **2.** The type of graph that shows how all of the parts relate to the whole is the bar graph.

_____ True _____   **3.** The graph which represents gradual or continuous changes is the curved-line graph.

_____ True _____   **4.** The expression $6x^2 - 2x + 12$ is a polynomial.

_____ False _____   **5.** The expression $5x^2yz$ contains four terms.

Write an equation for the following problems and solve. *(–3 each)*

$x + 3x = 92$ or $x + \frac{1}{3}x = 92$

_____

23, 69

6. Separate 92 into two parts, one of which is $\frac{1}{3}$ of the other.

_____ $x + 3x = 420$ _____

_____ 105 miles _____

7. Mary and her father took an all-day automobile ride, going 3 times as far in the afternoon as in the morning. In all they traveled 420 miles. How far did they travel in the morning?

_____ $x + 2x - 12 = 42$ _____

_____ 18 girls; 24 boys _____

8. In a class of 42 students, the number of boys is 12 fewer than twice the number of girls. Find the number of boys and girls.

Write in abbreviated form. *(–3 each)*

b^2d^4	**9.** *bbdddd*
$4a^3bc^2$	**10.** *4aaabcc*
m^4s^2t	**11.** *mmmmmsst*
$6a^3b$	**12.** *6aaab*

Find the value of each of the following expressions when $x = 3$, $y = 2$, $m = 4$, $n = 1$, and $a = 0$. *(–3 each)*

24	**13.** xy^3
36	**14.** $(y + m)^2$
2	**15.** $\frac{m^2}{4y} + \frac{ax}{7m}$
8	**16.** $m + xy - m \div y$
15	**17.** $(m - n)(x + y)$

Collect and unite similar terms. *(–3 each)*

$3a^2 + 2a + 1$	**18.** $5a^2 + a + 4 + 3a - 2a^2 - 3 - 2a$
$9a + 3b$	**19.** $7a + b + 5b - 2a - 3b + 4a$
$4x^2 + 4x + 4$	**20.** $3x^2 + x + 6 - x^2 + 5x - 4 + 2x^2 - 2x + 2$
$4mn + 11$	**21.** $8mn + 10 - 6mn + 2mn - 5 - 2 + 8$

LITERAL EQUATIONS: Write an equation to solve for the variable indicated. *(–4 each)*

_____ $r = \dfrac{i}{pt}$ _____ **22.** Solve for r in the formula $i = prt$.

_____ $r = \dfrac{C}{2\pi}$ _____ **23.** Solve for r in the formula $C = 2\pi r$.

$b = \dfrac{P - 2a}{2}$ or $b = \dfrac{P}{2} - a$ **24.** Solve for b in the formula $P = 2a + 2b$.

_____ $h = \dfrac{2A}{b + b'}$ _____ **25.** Solve for h in the formula $A = \frac{1}{2}h(b + b')$.

Solve each formula for the variable indicated. *(–4 each)*

_____ 24 sq. in. _____ **26.** Find A in the formula $A = bh$ when $b = 6$ in. and $h = 4$ in.

_____ 60 sq. in. _____ **27.** Find A in the formula $A = \frac{1}{2}h(b + b')$ when $h = 6$ in., $b = 12$ in., and $b' = 8$ in.

_____ 20° _____ **28.** Find C in the formula $C = \frac{5}{9}(F - 32°)$ when $F = 68°$.

_____ 5 _____ **29.** Find l in the formula $V = lwh$ when $V = 70$, $w = 7$, and $h = 2$.

QUIZ 10

Algebra 1

Sections 5.1–5.6
(–8 each)

Write the absolute value.

_____14_____   **1.** –14

_____25_____   **2.** +25

Choose the number that is greater.

_____–8_____   **3.** –10 or –8

_____0_____   **4.** 0 or –5

Draw a number line to show each addition.

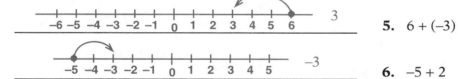

5. 6 + (–3)

6. –5 + 2

Find each answer.

_____–17_____   **7.** –3 + (–14)

_____–6_____   **8.** –12 + 8 + (–6) + 2 + 2

_____26_____   **9.** 20 – (–6)

_____–6_____   **10.** 8 – 14

QUIZ 11 _____ *Algebra 1*

Sections 5.7–5.9
(–8 each)

Combine each into a single number.

_____ −3 _____   **1.** $-9 + 10 - 4 =$

_____ 0 _____   **2.** $-8 - 3 + 6 - 2 + 14 - 7 =$

_____ 4 _____   **3.** $2 + 3 - 4 + 1 - 7 - 6 + 15 =$

Perform the indicated operations.

_____ −48 _____   **4.** $(-2)(-3)(-8) =$

_____ −20 _____   **5.** $3 \cdot (-5)(-4) \div 6 \cdot (-2) =$

_____ 8 _____   **6.** $8 \div (-2) \cdot (-6) \cdot (-3) \div (-9) =$

_____ −36 _____   **7.** $-(6)(6) =$

_____ −125 _____   **8.** $(-5)(-5)(-5) =$

_____ 64 _____   **9.** $(-8)(-8) =$

Solve the word problem.

_____ 24 _____   **10.** Some number increased by $\frac{2}{3}$ of itself equals 40. What is the number?

$$x = \text{number}$$

$$x + \frac{2}{3}x = 40$$

$$1\frac{2}{3}x = 40$$

$$\frac{5}{3}x = 40$$

$$x = 24$$

QUIZ 12   *Algebra 1*

Sections 6.1–6.4
(–8 each)

Add.

_____2a_____ **1.** $6a + 3a - 7a$

_____$-7y$_____ **2.** $7y - 6y + 2y - 8y - 3y + y$

_____$8a^2b - 9b^2c$_____ **3.** $14a^2b + 3ab^2 - 7b^2c - 3ab^2 - 6a^2b - 5b^2c + 3b^2c$

_____$-x - 5y - z$_____ **4.** $3x - 2y + 2y - 3z + 2z - 4x - 5y$

Subtract.

5. $3x$
    $\underline{-\ 6x}$
    $9x$

6. $14m^2$
    $\underline{-\ 11m^2}$
    $25m^2$

7. $3(y - 2)$
    $\underline{-\ 3(y - 2)}$
    $6(y - 2)$

8. $-7x^2y$
    $\underline{-\ 8x^2y}$
    x^2y

Add $5x^5 + 3x^4 - 2x^3 + 1$ to each polynomial.

$\underline{5x^5 + 6x^4 - 4x^3 + 3x + 8}$ **9.** $3x^4 - 2x^3 + 3x + 7$

$\underline{4x^5 + 2x^4 - 2x^3 + 8x^2 + 9}$ **10.** $-x^5 - x^4 + 8x^2 + 8$

QUIZ 13 _____ *Algebra 1*

Subtract the following from $6x^2 - 2xy + 3y^2$.

____$2x^2 + xy + 5y^2$____   **1.** $4x^2 - 3xy - 2y^2$

____$7x^2 - xy + 4y^2$____   **2.** $-x^2 - xy - y^2$

____$8x^2 - 6xy + 10y^2$____   **3.** $-2x^2 + 4xy - 7y^2$

Let $x = a^2 - b^2$; $y = ab$; $z = a^2 + b^2$.

____$2a^2 + ab$____   **4.** $x + y + z$

____$ab - 2a^2$____   **5.** $y - x - z$

Solve for x.

____$x = 23$____   **6.** $x - 6 = 17$

____$x = 28$____   **7.** $\frac{2x + 4}{3} = 13 + 7$

____$x = -13$____   **8.** $4x + 5 = 3x - 8$

____$x = 11$____   **9.** $6x - 10 = 4(x + 3)$

Solve the word problem.

_$a = 7$ in., $b = 9$ in., $c = 9$ in._   **10.** The sides of a triangle have these lengths: $2x + 3$, $4x + 1$, and $x + 7$. The perimeter is 25 inches. Find the length of each side using the formula $P = a + b + c$.

$$P = a + b + c \qquad\qquad 2 \cdot 2 + 3 = 7 \text{ in.}$$
$$25 = 2x + 3 + 4x + 1 + x + 7 \qquad 4 \cdot 2 + 1 = 9 \text{ in.}$$
$$25 = 7x + 11 \qquad\qquad 2 + 7 = 9 \text{ in.}$$
$$14 = 7x$$
$$2 = x$$

31

QUIZ 14

Name three grouping symbols.

_____ **1.** Three of the following: parentheses, brackets, braces, bar

_____ **2.**

_____ **3.**

Write plus or minus.

_____minus_____ **4.** The sign that precedes a parenthesis that causes the sign of each term within the parenthesis to change when the parenthesis is removed.

_____plus_____ **5.** The sign that precedes a parenthesis that causes no sign changes when the parenthesis is removed.

Remove the parentheses.

_____$-8x + 4y - 2z$_____ **6.** $-(8x - 4y + 2z)$

_____$8x - 4y + 2z$_____ **7.** $(8x - 4y + 2z)$

Simplify by removing the parentheses.

_____$x + 7y$_____ **8.** $3x - (2x - 7y)$

_____$2x^2 - 5xy + 3y^2$_____ **9.** $4x^2 - 2xy + y^2 - (2xy + 3x^2 - 3y^2) + (x^2 - xy - y^2)$

_____0_____ **10.** $xy - [xy + xz - x - (2x - xz) + 2x - 2xz] - x$

Name _____ Date _____ Score _____

TEST 3 (Nine-Weeks Exam) _____ *Algebra 1*

Units 5–6.8

DIRECTIONS: Show all of your work neatly in pencil in the space provided. Copy your
answers from your work space into the space provided for the answer. Use another
sheet to keep all work and answers covered at all times.

Combine each into a single number. *(–3 each)*

_____–11_____	**1.** $8 + 2 + 3 - 9 - 7 + 4 - 12$
_____0_____	**2.** $- 8 - 3 + 6 - 2 + 14 - 7$
_____12_____	**3.** $7 + 6 + 2 - 3 - 5 - 9 + 14$

Subtract the lower number from the upper number. *(–3 each)*

_____–5_____	**4.** $\begin{array}{r} 7 \\ \underline{12} \end{array}$
_____7_____	**5.** $\begin{array}{r} -8 \\ \underline{-15} \end{array}$
_____–27_____	**6.** $\begin{array}{r} -11 \\ \underline{16} \end{array}$
_____19_____	**7.** $\begin{array}{r} 14 \\ \underline{-5} \end{array}$

Perform the operation indicated. *(–3 each)*

_____–24_____	**8.** $(-8)(3)$
_____84_____	**9.** $(-7)(2)(3)(-2)$
_____–24_____	**10.** $(2)(-4)(-3)(-1)$
_____5_____	**11.** $\frac{-35}{-7}$
_____–8_____	**12.** $\frac{48}{-6}$
_____–6_____	**13.** $9 \div (-3)(-4)(5) \div (-10)$
_____8_____	**14.** $8 \div (-2)(-6)(-3) \div (-9)$

(cont.)

Perform the operation indicated. *(–2 each)*

+10	**15.** $3 \, (-5) \, (-4) \div 6$
+49	**16.** $(-7)^2$
–25	**17.** -5^2
–27	**18.** $(-3)^3$

Write in algebraic form. *(–2 each)*

$6x + 4$	**19.** Four more than six times x
$\dfrac{2x}{3} - 6$	**20.** 6 less than the quotient of $2x$ divided by 3
$xy - 5$	**21.** 5 less than the product of x and y
$25 - n$	**22.** n less than 25

Simplify. *(–2 each)*

$-2x - 7y$	**23.** $5x - (7x + 7y)$
$3a - 8c$	**24.** $(2a + 3b - 4c) + (a - 3b - 4c)$
$x^2 - 6xy + 4y^2$	**25.** $(2x^2 - 4xy + y^2) - (x^2 + 2xy - 3y^2)$
$-4a + 3b + 8y - 5$	**26.** $y - [5 - 3b - (7y - 4a)]$

Solve each equation for *x*. *(−2 each)*

_____ $x = 7$ _____	**27.** $3x - 12 = 9$
_____ $x = 18$ _____	**28.** $\frac{2x}{3} = 12$
_____ $x = 1$ _____	**29.** $13x + 4 = 5x + 12$
_____ $x = 2$ _____	**30.** $46 + 3x - 60 = 5x - 10 - 4x$
_____ $x = 3$ _____	**31.** $10x - 39 + 12x - 9x + 42 - 4x = 42 - 4x$

Perform the operation indicated. *(−2 each)*

_____ ab _____	**32.** $3ab - 4ab + 7ab - 6ab + 4ab - 3ab$
_____ $18(a - b)$ _____	**33.** $11(a - b) - 2(a - b) - 1(a - b) + 10(a - b)$
_____ $20r - 5s - 12t$ _____	**34.** $15r + 6s - 11t + r - 9s + t - 2s + 5r - 2t - r$

Subtract. *(−2 each)*

_____ $7xy - 7y^2$ _____	**35.** From $6x^2 + 4xy - 3y^2$ subtract $6x^2 - 3xy + 4y^2$.
_____ $-ab$ _____	**36.** From $3ab + a^2 + b^2$ subtract $a^2 + 4ab + b^2$.

(cont.)

Write an equation for the following problems and solve. *(−2 each part)*

$\underline{3x = (x + 1) + (x + 2) + 8}$ **37.** Find three consecutive numbers such that 3 times the first is equal to 8 more than the sum of the other two.

$\underline{\hspace{1cm} 11,\ 12,\ 13 \hspace{1cm}}$

$\underline{\hspace{1cm} x + \frac{1}{5}x = 12 \hspace{1cm}}$ **38.** If $\frac{1}{5}$ of a number is added to the number the sum is 12. Find the number.

$\underline{\hspace{1.2cm} 10 \hspace{1.2cm}}$

QUIZ 15   *Algebra 1*

Write *true* or *false*.

_____ true _____   **1.** $x^2 - y^2 - 2xy + c = x^2 - (y^2 + 2xy - c)$

_____ false _____   **2.** $-3ab + 4ac - 2ad = -(3ab + 4ac + 2ad)$

_____ false _____   **3.** $a^2 + ab - 2b^2 = -(a^2 - ab + 2b^2)$

_____ false _____   **4.** $a^3 - a^2 + a - 1 = (a^3 - a^2) - (a + 1)$

_____ true _____   **5.** $a^2 - b^2 + 2ab - c^2 = a^2 - (b^2 - 2ab + c^2)$

Group as a subtrahend the last three terms.

$6m^3 - (4m^2 - 2m + 1)$ **6.** $6m^3 - 4m^2 + 2m - 1$

$x^2 - (-2xy - y^2 + z^2)$ **7.** $x^2 + 2xy + y^2 - z^2$

$x^3 - (3x^2y - 3xy^2 + y^3)$ **8.** $x^3 - 3x^2y + 3xy^2 - y^3$

Represent algebraically.

_____ $10 - x$ _____ 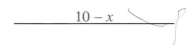   **9.** If 10 is separated into two parts, one of which is x, represent the second part.

_____ $2x + 3$ _____ 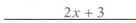   **10.** If $2x + 1$ is the first odd number, what is the second odd number?

39

QUIZ 16 _____ *Algebra 1*

Sections 6.10–6.12
(–8 each)

Answer the questions about $-4x^3(2x^2)$.

____negative____ **1.** What is the sign of the product?

____multiplication____ **2.** What process (addition or multiplication) is used to find the numerical coefficient of the product?

____addition____ **3.** What process (addition or multiplication) is used to find the exponents of the product?

Multiply.

____$-6a^2b^2$____ **4.** $(2ab)(-3ab)$

____$12a^5b^5c^9$____ **5.** $(-3a^3b^2c^4)(-4a^2b^3c^5)$

____$10x^2 - 15x + 20$____ **6.** $5(2x^2 - 3x + 4)$

____$-3x^5y - 6x^4y + 3x^3y - 3x^2y$____ **7.** $-3x^2y(x^3 + 2x^2 - x + 1)$

____$x^2 + x - 6$____ **8.** $(x + 3)(x - 2)$

____$6b^2 - 7b - 5$____ **9.** $(2b + 1)(3b - 5)$

Solve the word problem.

____5, 6, 7____ **10.** Find 3 consecutive numbers such that 4 times the first is equal to 7 more than the sum of the other two.

$$x = \text{1st number} \qquad\qquad x + 1 = 6$$
$$x + 1 = \text{2nd number} \qquad\qquad x + 2 = 7$$
$$x + 2 = \text{3rd number}$$
$$4x = x + 1 + x + 2 + 7$$
$$4x = 2x + 10$$
$$2x = 10$$
$$x = 5$$

QUIZ 17

Algebra 1

Section 6.13
(–9 each)

Write in ascending order.

$\underline{1 - 3x - x^2 + x^3 + 2x^4}$ **1.** $x^3 + 2x^4 - x^2 + 1 - 3x$

$\underline{-6 + 2b + 4b^2}$ **2.** $4b^2 - 6 + 2b$

Write in descending order.

$\underline{-x^4 - x^3 + x^2 + x + 3}$ **3.** $x^2 - x^4 + 3 - x^3 + x$

$\underline{a^2 + a + 1}$ **4.** $a + 1 + a^2$

Write the factor that is shared by both terms.

$\underline{x}$ **5.** $bx - cx$

$\underline{y}$ **6.** $amy + rby$

$\underline{z}$ **7.** $(2x - y)z + (2y + x)z$

Add by uniting the literal coefficients.

$\underline{(a + b)x}$ **8.** $ax + bx$

$\underline{(1 - b)x}$ **9.** $x - bx$

$\underline{x(a - b - c) - y(a - d + e)}$ **10.** $ax - bx - cx - ay + dy - ey$

Name _____ Date _____ Score _____

QUIZ 18

Algebra 1

Sections 6.14–6.15
(–9 each)

Answer the questions about $\frac{-16x^5}{4x^3}$.

<u>negative</u>	**1.** What is the sign of the quotient?
<u>division</u>	**2.** What process (division or subtraction) is used to get the numerical coefficient of the quotient?
<u>subtraction</u>	**3.** What process (division or subtraction) is used to get the exponents of the quotient?

Find each answer.

a	**4.** $\frac{a^6}{a^5}$
1	**5.** $\frac{a^6}{a^6}$
$\frac{1}{a}$ or a^{-1}	**6.** $\frac{a^6}{a^7}$
$-8x^2z$	**7.** $\frac{-16x^3y^2z^5}{2xy^2z^4}$
$-3a^3 + 2b^2$	**8.** $\frac{15a^4b - 10ab^3}{-5ab}$
$\frac{x}{8y}$ or $\frac{\frac{1}{8}x}{y}$	**9.** $\frac{\frac{1}{2}x^2y^3}{4xy^4}$
$6x^4 - 4x^6yz + 9x^9z$	**10.** $\frac{24x^5y^2z - 16x^7y^3z^2 + 36x^{10}y^2z^2}{4xy^2z}$

45

QUIZ 19 *Algebra 1*

Arrange the divisor in descending order, and then arrange the dividend in descending order.

_____ $m + 6$ _____ **1.** $6 + m \overline{\smash{\big)}\, m^2 - 18 - 3m}$

_____ $m^2 - 3m - 18$ _____ **2.**

Find each quotient.

_____ $x + 9$ _____

3. $x + 4 \overline{\smash{\big)}\, x^2 + 13x + 36}$

$\underline{x^2 + 4x}$

$9x + 36$

_____ $x - 6$ _____ **4.** $\underline{9x + 36}$

4. $x - 5 \overline{\smash{\big)}\, x^2 - 11x + 30}$

$\underline{x^2 - 5x}$

$-6x + 30$

$\underline{-6x + 30}$

quotient for 3: $x + 9$; quotient for 4: $x - 6$

Find each product.

_____ $-54a^7 b$ _____ **5.** $9a^5(-6a^2 b)$

_____ $a^2 b^2 c + ab^2 c^2 + abc^2 d$ _____ **6.** $abc(ab + bc + cd)$

_____ $x^2 + 9x + 18$ _____

7. $x + 3$

$\underline{x + 6}$

$x^2 + 3x$

_____ $x^4 - 6x^3 + 3x^2 + 26x - 24$ _____ **8.** $\underline{+ 6x + 18}$

$x^2 + 9x + 18$

8. $x^3 - 3x^2 - 6x + 8$

$\underline{x - 3}$

$x^4 - 3x^3 - 6x^2 + 8x$

$\underline{- 3x^3 + 9x^2 + 18x - 24}$

$x^4 - 6x^3 + 3x^2 + 26x - 24$

Express algebraically.

_____ $50 - x$ _____ **9.** What number is x less than 50?

_____ $y - x$ _____ **10.** Ben had y dollars. He gave x dollars to Mrs. Howe. How many dollars does Ben have now?

TEST 4 _____ *Algebra 1*

Sections 6.8–6.17

DIRECTIONS: Show all of your work neatly in pencil in the space provided. Copy your answers from your work space into the space provided for the answer. Use another sheet to keep all work and answers covered at all times.

TRUE-FALSE: If the statement is always true, write *true* in the space; if the statement is *not* always true, write *false* in the space. *(–4 each)*

false	**1.** $25^0 = 0$
false	**2.** $a^5 \cdot a^2 = a^{10}$
true	**3.** $a^8 \div a^4 = a^4$
false	**4.** $4a - (-2a) = 2a$
false	**5.** $2x(3x + 4) = 6x + 8$

Write an algebraic expression for each statement. *(–4 each)*

$25 - n$	**6.** What number is n less than 25?
$50 - x$	**7.** If 50 is separated into two parts, one of which is x, represent the other part.
$x - m$	**8.** John has x dollars and gives Sam m dollars. Represent what John has left.
$xy(x + y - d)$	**9.** Indicate the product of xy and $x + y - d$.
$x = d(y - c)$	**10.** Write an equation that x equals d times $(y - c)$.

Multiply. *(–3 each)*

$-28x^3$	**11.** $\begin{array}{r} 4x^2 \\ -\ 7x \end{array}$
$27xy^3z$	**12.** $\begin{array}{r} -3xy^2 \\ -9yz \end{array}$
$x^2y^2z + xy^2z^2 + x^2yz^2$	**13.** $\begin{array}{r} xy + yz + xz \\ xyz \end{array}$

(cont.)

Multiply (cont.)

$-12x^5 - 18x^4 - 6x^3 - 3x^2$ **14.** $\begin{array}{l} 4x^3 + 6x^2 + 2x + 1 \\ \underline{-\ 3x^2} \end{array}$

$x^2 + 10x + 24$ **15.** $\begin{array}{l} x + 4 \\ \underline{x + 6} \end{array}$

$x^4 - 6x^3 + x^2 + 24x - 20$ **16.** $\begin{array}{l} x^3 - 4x^2 - 7x + 10 \\ \underline{x - 2} \end{array}$

Divide. *(–3 each)*

$5a^2b^3$ **17.** $\dfrac{-20a^4b^5y^2}{-4a^2b^2y^2}$

$-4a^3y^2z^2$ **18.** $\dfrac{-36a^4y^2z^3}{9az}$

$4r + 5 - 7s$ **19.** $\dfrac{24r^3s^2 + 30r^2s^2 - 42r^2s^3}{6r^2s^2}$

$-3a - 5bc$ **20.** $\dfrac{36a^3b^4c^6 + 60a^2b^5c^7}{-12a^2b^4c^6}$

$3a^2 - 2a + 3$ **21.** $a + 4\overline{)3a^3 + 10a^2 - 5a + 12}$

In each expression, group the last three terms in parentheses. *(−3 each)*

$a + (b - c + d)$
or $a - (-b + c - d)$ **22.** $a + b - c + d$

$w - (x - y + z)$
or $w + (-x + y - z)$ **23.** $w - x + y - z$

$a^2 - b^2 + (c - d + e)$
or $a^2 - b^2 - (-c + d - e)$ **24.** $a^2 - b^2 + c - d + e$

Write an equation for the following problems and solve. *(−2 each part)*

$x + x + 1 + x + 2 = 99$ **25.** Find three consecutive numbers whose sum is 99.

32, 33, 34

$x + x + 8 = 36$ **26.** If one piece of a yardstick is 8 inches longer than the other, how long is each?

14″ , 22″

$36 - 8 = 28 \div 2 = 14$ $\begin{array}{r} 14 \\ + 8 \\ \hline 22 \end{array}$

QUIZ 20 _____ *Algebra 1*

Fill in the missing term. Include the sign.

_____+12_____ **1.** $(2x + 6)(3x + 2) = 6x^2 + 22x$ __?__

_____+15_____ **2.** $(y - 3)(2y - 5) = 2y^2 - 11y$ __?__

_____$15x^2$_____ **3.** $(5x - 2y)(3x - 3y) =$ __?__ $-21xy + 6y^2$

_____+22x_____ **4.** $(2x + 6)(3x + 2) = 6x^2$ __?__ $+ 12$

_____+49xy_____ **5.** $(5y + 3x)(3y + 8x) = 15y^2$ __?__ $+ 24x^2$

_____$12x^2$_____ **6.** $(4x + 3)(3x + 2) =$ __?__ $+ 17x + 6$

_____$-8x$_____ **7.** $(x - 6)(x - 2) = x^2$ __?__ $+ 12$

_____+6_____ **8.** $(3x - 2)(2x - 3) = 6x^2 - 13x$ __?__

_____+29ab_____ **9.** $(2a + 5b)(5a + 2b) = 10a^2$ __?__ $+ 10b^2$

_____$-14x$_____ **10.** $(2x - 6)(3x + 2) = 6x^2$ __?__ $- 12$

Name _____ Date _____ Score _____

Sections 7.3–7.4
(–9 each)

Write _true_ or _false_.

_____false_____   **1.** $7^0 = 0$

_____false_____   **2.** $x^3 \cdot x^4 = x^{12}$

_____true_____   **3.** $x^8 \div x^4 = x^4$

_____false_____   **4.** $6a - (-3a) = 3a$

Find each product. Use the FOIL method.

_____$x^2 + x - 12$_____   **5.** $(x + 4)(x - 3)$

_____$6x^2 + 7x - 20$_____   **6.** $(2x + 5)(3x - 4)$

_____$x^4 - y^2$_____   **7.** $(x^2 + y)(x^2 - y)$

__$.04x^2 + .08xy + .03y^2$__   **8.** $(.2x + .3y)(.2x + .1y)$

$x^4y^8 + 2bcx^2y^4 + b^2c^2$ **9.** $(x^2y^4 + bc)(x^2y^4 + bc)$

Solve the word problem.

_____5 in. and 7 in._____   **10.** A foot-long hot dog is cut into two parts. One part is 2 inches longer than the other part. How long are the two parts?

$$x = \text{1st part} \qquad \text{5 in.}$$
$$x + 2 = \text{2nd part} \qquad \text{7 in.}$$
$$x + x + 2 = 12$$
$$2x + 2 = 12$$
$$2x = 10$$
$$x = 5$$

QUIZ 22

Algebra 1

Sections 7.5–7.6
(–9 each)

Tell whether the product is a binomial or trinomial.

___trinomial___   **1.** $(x - 2)^2$

___binomial___   **2.** $(x + 2)(x - 2)$

Give the sign of the middle term of the product.

___positive___   **3.** $(x + 2)^2$

___negative___   **4.** $(x - 2)^2$

Answer each question.

___positive___   **5.** What is always the sign of the first term and the last term in the product when a binomial is squared?

___negative___   **6.** What is always the sign of the last term in the product when a sum and difference are multiplied?

Find each product.

___$9x^2 - 12xy + 4y^2$___   **7.** $(3x - 2y)^2$

___$x^2 - x + \frac{1}{4}$___   **8.** $(x - \frac{1}{2})^2$

___$16x^4 - 9b^4$___   **9.** $(4x^2 + 3b^2)(4x^2 - 3b^2)$

___$\frac{1}{4}a^2 - 4$___   **10.** $(\frac{1}{2}a + 2)(\frac{1}{2}a - 2)$

QUIZ 23 _____ *Algebra 1*

Write the common monomial factor.

_____$2x^2$_____ **1.** $2x^5 - 8x^3 + 6x^2$

_____$x - y$_____ **2.** $3(x - y) + 2(x - y)$

Complete the factored form.

_____5_____ **3.** $5c + 5d = \underline{\ ?\ }(c + d)$

_____7_____ **4.** $3x^2 - 17x - 28 = (3x + 4)(x - \underline{\ ?\ })$

_____$2x$ and $2x$_____ **5.** $4x^2 + 8x - 21 = (\underline{\ ?\ } + 7)(\underline{\ ?\ } - 3)$

_____3 and 7_____ **6.** $15x^2 + 44x + 21 = (5x + \underline{\ ?\ })(3x + \underline{\ ?\ })$

_____$x + 4$_____ **7.** $4x^2 + 19x + 12 = (4x + 3)(\underline{\ ?\ })$

_____6 and $x - 2$_____ **8.** $7x^2 - 8x - 12 = (7x + \underline{\ ?\ })(\underline{\ ?\ })$

_____$(3x - 1)(2x - 3)$_____ **9.** $6x^2 - 11x + 3 = (\underline{\ ?\ })(\underline{\ ?\ })$

Solve the word problem.

_____7 and 40_____ **10.** Mrs. Hill is 33 years older than her son. In 4 years, she will be four times as old as her son. How old is each?

$$x = \text{son's age}$$
$$x + 33 = \text{Mrs. Hill's age}$$
$$4(x + 4) = x + 33 + 4$$
$$4x + 16 = x + 37$$
$$3x = 21$$
$$x = 7$$

QUIZ 24   *Algebra 1*

Write the missing term.

_____8_____   **1.** $x^2 - 16x + 64 = (x - 8)(x - \underline{\ ?\ })$

_____$x + 9$_____   **2.** $x^2 - 81 = (\underline{\ ?\ })(x - 9)$

_____$x - \frac{1}{3}$_____   **3.** $x^2 - \frac{1}{9} = (x + \frac{1}{3})(\underline{\ ?\ })$

_____$5x^3 + 11y^5$_____   **4.** $25x^6 - 121y^{10} = (\underline{\ ?\ })(5x^3 - 11y^5)$

Factor.

_____$2x^2(4x - 3)$_____   **5.** $8x^3 - 6x^2$

_____$(c + 2)(c - 2)$_____   **6.** $c^2 - 4$

___$3x(x^2 + 1)(x + 1)(x - 1)$___   **7.** $3x^5 - 3x$

_____$(x + 9)(x + 2)$_____   **8.** $x^2 + 11x + 18$

_____$4(x + 4)(x + 3)$_____   **9.** $4x^2 + 28x + 48$

_____$2(x - 5)(x - 1)$_____   **10.** $2x^2 - 12x + 10$

Name _____ Date _____ Score _____

TEST 5 _____ *Algebra 1*

Sections 7.1–7.9

DIRECTIONS: Show all of your work neatly in pencil in the space provided. Copy your answers from your work space into the space provided for the answer. Use another sheet to keep all work and answers covered at all times.

Multiply. *(–3 each)*

$\underline{\hspace{2em} 4x + 4y \hspace{2em}}$ **1.** $4(x + y)$

$\underline{\hspace{2em} 3x^2 - 6x \hspace{2em}}$ **2.** $3x(x - 2)$

$\underline{5ax^3 - 10a^2x^2 + 5a^3x}$ **3.** $5ax(x^2 - 2ax + a^2)$

$\underline{\hspace{2em} 12a^2 - 13a - 35 \hspace{2em}}$ **4.** $(3a - 7)(4a + 5)$

$\underline{\hspace{2em} 15x^2 - 21xy + 6y^2 \hspace{2em}}$ **5.** $(5x - 2y)(3x - 3y)$

$\underline{\hspace{2em} 21z^2 + 11az - 2a^2 \hspace{2em}}$ **6.** $(7z - a)(3z + 2a)$

$\underline{\hspace{2em} 9a^2b^2 - 100c^4 \hspace{2em}}$ **7.** $(3ab + 10c^2)(3ab - 10c^2)$

$\underline{\hspace{2em} x^2 + 11x + 30 \hspace{2em}}$ **8.** $(x + 5)(x + 6)$

$\underline{\hspace{2em} x^2 + x - 56 \hspace{2em}}$ **9.** $(x - 7)(x + 8)$

$\underline{\hspace{2em} y^2 + 6y + 9 \hspace{2em}}$ **10.** $(y + 3)^2$

$\underline{\hspace{2em} 16x^2y^2 - 56xy + 49 \hspace{2em}}$ **11.** $(4xy - 7)^2$

$\underline{\hspace{2em} y^2 - \frac{1}{2}y + \frac{1}{16} \hspace{2em}}$ **12.** $(y - \frac{1}{4})^2$

$\underline{\hspace{2em} 9m^2 - n^2 \hspace{2em}}$ **13.** $(3m + n)(3m - n)$

$20r^4 - 23r^3t - 11r^2t^2 + 11rt^3 + 3t^4$ **14.** $\underline{\begin{array}{l} 4r^2 - 3rt - t^2 \\ 5r^2 - 2rt - 3t^2 \end{array}}$

Factor. *(–3 each)*

$5x^2(6 - x)$ **15.** $30x^2 - 5x^3$

$4a^2(3a^2 - 5a + 1)$ **16.** $12a^4 - 20a^3 + 4a^2$

$4t(m - n)(m - n)$ **17.** $4m^2t - 8mnt + 4n^2t$

$(x + 3)(x + 4)$ **18.** $x^2 + 7x + 12$

$(x - 2)(x - 6)$ **19.** $x^2 - 8x + 12$

$(c - 9)(c + 8)$ **20.** $c^2 - c - 72$

$(3x + 2)(x - 3)$ **21.** $3x^2 - 7x - 6$

$(5x - 1)(x + 2)$ **22.** $5x^2 + 9x - 2$

$(5x + 2)(3x - 4)$ **23.** $15x^2 - 14x - 8$

$(3x + 5)(2x - 7)$ **24.** $6x^2 - 11x - 35$

$(x - y)^2$ **25.** $x^2 - 2xy + y^2$

$(x + 3)^2$ **26.** $x^2 + 6x + 9$

$(3x + y)^2$ **27.** $9x^2 + 6xy + y^2$

$(m - 4)^2$ **28.** $m^2 - 8m + 16$

Divide. *(–2 points)*

$\underline{2x^2 + 5x - 7}$ **29.** $2x - 3 \overline{\smash{)}\,4x^3 + 4x^2 - 29x + 21}$

Write an equation for the following problems and solve. *(–1 each part)*

$\underline{2x + 2x + 2 + 2x + 4 + 2x + 6 = 156}$ **30.** Find four consecutive even numbers whose sum is 156.

$\underline{36,\ 38,\ 40,\ 42}$

$\underline{3(x + 11) = x + 28 + 11}$ **31.** Mr. Jones is 28 years older than his son. In 11 years he will be 3 times as old as his son. How old is each now?

$\underline{\text{Mr. Jones: 31; son: 3}}$

Name _____ Date _____ Score _____

QUIZ 25

Algebra 1

Section 7.11
(–8 each)

Write *yes* if a sum and difference. Write *no* if not.

_____yes_____   **1.** $x^2 - y^2$

_____yes_____   **2.** $x^2 - (a + b)^2$

_____no_____   **3.** $x^3 - y^3$

_____no_____   **4.** $x^4 + (a + b)^2$

_____no_____   **5.** $x^2 - 2xy - y^2$

Write *yes* if a perfect square trinomial. Write *no* if not.

_____yes_____   **6.** $x^2 - 18x + 81$

_____no_____   **7.** $81a^2 + 9a + 1$

_____no_____   **8.** $x^2 - \frac{1}{8}x + \frac{1}{4}$

_____no_____   **9.** $16x^2 - 20xy + 9y$

Factor.

____$4(4a + b)(a - b)$____   **10.** $25a^2 - (3a + 2b)^2$

$(5a + 3a + 2b)(5a - 3a - 2b)$
$(8a + 2b)(2a - 2b)$
$2(4a + b) \cdot 2(a - b)$
$4(4a + b)(a - b)$

____$(2a - b + c)(2a - b - c)$____   **11.** $4a^2 - 4ab + b^2 - c^2$

$(2a - b)^2 - c^2$
$(2a - b + c)(2a - b - c)$

Name _____ Date _____ Score _____

QUIZ 26 _____ *Algebra 1*

Section 7.12
(−8 each)

Factor.

_____ $2(x + 9)(x - 9)$ _____   **1.** $2x^2 - 162$

_____ $3(x - 3)(x - 4)$ _____   **2.** $3x^2 - 21x + 36$

_____ $(x - 10)(x + 2)$ _____   **3.** $x^2 - 8x - 20$

$(x - 3)^2$ or $(x - 3)(x - 3)$ **4.** $x^2 - 6x + 9$

_____ $(a + 5)(a - 5)$ _____   **5.** $a^2 - 25$

_____ $2(x + 3)(x - 3)$ _____   **6.** $2x^2 - 18$

_____ $(x^2 + 4)(x + 2)(x - 2)$ _____   **7.** $x^4 - 16$

_____ $x(x + y)(x - y)$ _____   **8.** $x^3 - xy^2$

_____ $(a + b + c)(a - b - c)$ _____   **9.** $a^2 - (b + c)^2$

_____ $(3c + b)(c - b)$ _____   **10.** $4c^2 - (b + c)^2$

Name _____ Date _____ Score _____

QUIZ 27

Algebra 1

Section 7.13
(−8 each)

Factor.

_____$(x + 6)(x + 2)$_____ **1.** $x^2 + 8x + 12$

_____$(a + 4)(a − 5)$_____ **2.** $a^2 − a − 20$

_____$(3xy + 5)(3xy − 5)$_____ **3.** $9x^2y^2 − 25$

_____$(m^2 + 1)(m + 1)(m − 1)$_____ **4.** $m^4 − 1$

_____$(x + 3)(x + 4)$_____ **5.** $x^2 + 7x + 12$

_____$2(2x + 3y)(2x − 3y)$_____ **6.** $8x^2 − 18y^2$

_____$x(a + 1)(a − 1)$_____ **7.** $a^2x − x$

_____$10(y + 4)(y − 3)$_____ **8.** $10y^2 + 10y − 120$

_____$(x − 3 + y)(x − 3 − y)$_____ **9.** $(x − 3)^2 − y^2$

_____$(y + 2)(x + 3)$_____ **10.** $y(x + 3) + 2(x + 3)$

Name _____ Date _____ Score _____

QUIZ 28   *Algebra 1*

Section 7.14
(–9 each)

Give the number of roots in each equation.

_____2_____   **1.** $2x^2 - 12 = 5x$

_____1_____   **2.** $3(2x + 6) - 5 = 9x + 4$

_____2_____   **3.** $x^2 = 64$

Get all the variables and constants on one side of the equation and zero on the other side.

___$x^2 + 2x - 35 = 0$___   **4.** $x^2 - 35 = -2x$

___$0 = x^2 - 10x + 25$___   **5.** $10x = x^2 + 25$

Solve for *x*.

___$x = 3$ $x = 3$___   **6.** $x^2 - 6x + 9 = 0$

___$x = -\frac{8}{3}$ $x = \frac{8}{3}$___   **7.** $9x^2 = 64$

___$x = -2$ $x = 2$___   **8.** $7x^2 - 28 = 0$

___$x = -\frac{3}{2}$ $x = 4$___   **9.** $2x^2 - 12 = 5x$

Solve the word problem.

_____5 and 7_____   **10.** Find two numbers whose product is 35 $x = $ 1st number
and whose sum is 12.

$$12 - x = \text{2nd number}$$
$$x(12 - x) = 35$$
$$12x - x^2 = 35$$
$$0 = x^2 - 12x + 35$$
$$0 = (x - 5)(x - 7)$$
$$x - 5 = 0 \qquad x - 7 = 0$$
$$x = 5 \qquad\qquad x = 7$$

     73

Name _____ Date _____ Score _____

TEST 6 (Semester Exam)   *Algebra 1*

                                                                              Units 1–7

DIRECTIONS: Show all of your work neatly in pencil in the space provided. Copy your answers from your work space into the space provided for the answer. Use another sheet to keep all work and answers covered at all times.

EQUATIONS: Solve for *x*. *(–2 each)*

_____9_____   **1.** $2x + 3x = 45$

_____20_____   **2.** $2x - 11 = 29$

_____18_____   **3.** $\frac{2x}{3} = 12$

_____2_____   **4.** $6x + 2x - 1 = 15$

_____8_____   **5.** $5x - 6 = 50 - 2x$

_____11_____   **6.** $2(3x - 5) = 4x + 12$

Add. *(–2 each)*

                                    $2a + 4b$
_____–3a + 5b_____   **7.** $-\ 6a - 2b$
                                    $\underline{\quad a + 3b}$

_____$5x^2 - 12y^2$_____   **8.** $4x^2 - 3xy + 5y^2 + 10\,xy - 17y^2 - 11x^2 - 5xy + 12x^2 - 2xy$

SUBTRACT: Subtract the lower number from the upper number. *(–2 each)*

_____$4x + 6y$_____   **9.** $\begin{array}{r} 8x - \ y \\ \underline{4x - 7y} \end{array}$

_____$12x - 11y + 11z$_____   **10.** $\begin{array}{r} 15x - 3y + 2z \\ \underline{3x + 8y - 9z} \end{array}$

Multiply. *(−2 each)*

           $6ax^2 - 10ay^2$ **11.** $2a(3x^2 - 5y^2)$

           $6x^2 + 22x + 12$ **12.** $(2x + 6)(3x + 2)$

           $15x^2 - 21xy + 6y^2$ **13.** $(5x - 2y)(3x - 3y)$

           $12a^2 + 6ab - 6b^2$ **14.** $(4a - 2b)(3a + 3b)$

           $a^2 - 6ab + 9b^2$ **15.** $(a - 3b)^2$

           $s^2 - \frac{6}{5}s + \frac{9}{25}$ **16.** $\left(s - \frac{3}{5}\right)^2$

    $2b^4 + 7b^3 - 27b^2 - 8b + 16$ **17.** $\begin{array}{r} b^2 + 5b - 4 \\ 2b^2 - 3b - 4 \\ \hline \end{array}$

Divide. *(−2 each)*

           $5a^2b^3$ **18.** $\dfrac{-20a^4b^5y^2}{-4a^2b^2y^2}$

           $-3xy - 5y$ **19.** $\dfrac{9x^2y^2 + 15xy^2}{-3xy}$

           $3a^2 - 2a + 3$ **20.** $a + 4 \overline{)\, 3a^3 + 10a^2 - 5a + 12}$

Factor.   *(–3 each)*

$(a + b)(a - b)$	**21.** $a^2 - b^2$
$3x^2(1 - 2y)$	**22.** $3x^2 - 6x^2y$
$(r + 6)(r + 2)$	**23.** $r^2 + 8r + 12$
$(y - 3)(y - 5)$	**24.** $y^2 - 8y + 15$
$(x + 4)(x - 6)$	**25.** $x^2 - 2x - 24$
$(5a + 1)(a + 3)$	**26.** $5a^2 + 16a + 3$
$(3x + 2y)(3x - 2y)$	**27.** $9x^2 - 4y^2$
$3x(x^2 + 1)(x + 1)(x - 1)$	**28.** $3x^5 - 3x$
$(a + b - c)(a - b + c)$	**29.** $a^2 - (b - c)^2$
$2(2x + 3)(3x - 4)$	**30.** $12x^2 + 2x - 24$

Write an equation for the following problems and solve.   *(–3 each)*

$x + \frac{1}{8}x = 54$

48

31. The sum of a number and $\frac{1}{8}$ of the number is 54. Find the number.

$2x + 2x + 4 + 22 = 3(2x + 2)$

20, 22, 24

32. Find three consecutive even numbers so that the sum of the first and third numbers is 22 less than three times the second number.

ALGEBRAIC EXPRESSIONS: Write an algebraic representation or expression which represents the following statements. *(–3 each)*

$48 - y$ **33.** If 48 is separated into two parts, and one of the parts is y, what is the other part?

$25 - n$ **34.** What is n less than 25?

$d - nc$ **35.** A boy has d dollars. He buys n notebooks at c dollars each. How many dollars does he have left?

$a - 10$ **36.** Beth read 10 pages in a book, stopping at the top of page a. On what page did she begin?

$2n + 3$
$2n + 5$ **37.** If $2n + 1$ is an odd number, what are the next two consecutive odd numbers?

QUIZ 29 *Algebra 1*

Sections 8.1–8.3
(–9 each)

Write with a *positive* numerator and denominator.

_____ $\dfrac{x}{y}$ **1.** $\dfrac{-x}{-y}$

_____ $-\dfrac{a}{b}$ **2.** $\dfrac{a}{-b}$

_____ $\dfrac{x}{y}$ **3.** $-\dfrac{-x}{y}$

_____ $-\dfrac{x}{a+b}$ **4.** $-\dfrac{-x}{-a-b}$

_____ $\dfrac{2(x+y)}{3(a+b)}$ **5.** $\dfrac{-2(-x-y)}{3(a+b)}$

Find each answer.

_____ $\dfrac{6}{7}$ **6.** Reduce $\dfrac{24}{28}$ to lowest terms.

_____ $\dfrac{3}{4}$ **7.** Simplify $\dfrac{\frac{2}{3}}{\frac{8}{9}}$.

_____ $\dfrac{7}{8}$ **8.** $\dfrac{1}{2}-\dfrac{3}{8}+\dfrac{3}{4}$

_____ 12 **9.** $5\dfrac{1}{4}\cdot 2\dfrac{2}{7}$

_____ $9\dfrac{2}{5}$ **10.** Change $\dfrac{47}{5}$ to a mixed number.

QUIZ 30 *Algebra 1*

Section 8.4
(–8 each)

Write with a *positive* numerator and denominator.

$\dfrac{a}{b}$ _____ 1. $\dfrac{-a}{-b}$

$\dfrac{x}{y}$ _____ 2. $-\dfrac{x}{-y}$

$-\dfrac{a}{a+b}$ _____ 3. $-\dfrac{-a}{-a-b}$

Reduce to *lowest* terms.

x _____ 4. $\dfrac{x^2y}{xy}$

$\dfrac{1}{4bc}$ _____ 5. $\dfrac{3b^3}{12b^4c}$

$-\dfrac{a}{6bd}$ _____ 6. $\dfrac{-7a^2bcd^3}{42ab^2cd^4}$

$\dfrac{1}{2x-3a}$ _____ 7. $\dfrac{2x}{4x^2-6ax}$

$\dfrac{a+2b}{c+3d}$ _____ 8. $\dfrac{5a+10b}{5c+15d}$

$\dfrac{a+b}{a-b}$ _____ 9. $\dfrac{(a+b)^2}{a^2-b^2}$

$\dfrac{b^3}{b+1}$ _____ 10. $\dfrac{3b^3}{3b+3}$

QUIZ 31 *Algebra 1*

Sections 8.5–8.7
(−8 each)

Change to the indicated denominator.

_____$\frac{2ax}{4ay}$_____ **1.** $\frac{x}{2y}$ $4ay$

_____$\frac{x-2}{x^2-4}$_____ **2.** $\frac{1}{x+2}$ x^2-4

$\frac{y^2(y+1)}{y^2+2y+1}$ or $\frac{y^3+y^2}{y^2+2y+1}$ **3.** $\frac{y^2}{y+1}$ y^2+2y+1

Write the least common denominator for the following fractions:

_____ab_____ **4.** $\frac{1}{a}, \frac{1}{b}$

_____abc_____ **5.** $\frac{x}{ab}, \frac{y}{bc}, \frac{z}{ac}$

_____$a(a+b)(a-b)$_____ **6.** $\frac{1}{a}, \frac{1}{a+b}, \frac{1}{a-b}$

_____$(x+y)(x-y)$_____ **7.** $\frac{a}{x^2-y^2}, \frac{b}{x+y}$

_____$x(x-2)(x-3)$_____ **8.** $\frac{12}{x^2-3x}, \frac{5}{x^2-5x+6}$

Change to an integral or mixed expression.

_____$3a$_____ **9.** $\frac{27a}{9}$

_____$a+\frac{b}{x}$_____ **10.** $\frac{ax+b}{x}$

QUIZ 32 _____ *Algebra 1*

Section 8.8
(−8 each)

What must the denominator be multiplied by to get the new denominator?

_____3_____ **1.** $\frac{3}{2x}$ $6x$

_____$x - y$_____ **2.** $\frac{1}{x - y}$ $(x - y)^2$

_____$x + y$_____ **3.** $\frac{1}{x - y}$ $x^2 - y^2$

Make equivalent fractions.

_____$8ab$_____ **4.** $\frac{4}{7a} = \frac{}{14a^2b}$

_____$a + b$_____ **5.** $\frac{1}{a + b} = \frac{}{a^2 + 2ab + b^2}$

_____$2(a + b)$_____ **6.** $\frac{2}{a - b} = \frac{}{a^2 - b^2}$

Perform the addition and subtraction.

_____$\frac{17a}{12}$_____ **7.** $\frac{2a}{3} + \frac{3a}{4}$

___$\frac{11}{6}$ or $1\frac{5}{6}$___ **8.** $\frac{3x + 4}{2x} + \frac{x - 6}{3x}$

_____$\frac{3x + 7}{6}$_____ **9.** $\frac{x + 2}{12} - \frac{x - 3}{3} + \frac{3x}{4}$

___$\frac{4 + 3ab - 2a}{12a}$___ **10.** $\frac{ab + b}{3ab} - \frac{2a - ab}{4a}$ $\frac{b(a + 1)}{3ab} - \frac{a(2 - b)}{4a}$

$\frac{a + 1}{3a} - \frac{2 - b}{4}$

$\frac{4a + 4 - 6a + 3ab}{12a}$

$\frac{4 + 3ab - 2a}{12a}$

Name _____   Date _____   Score _____

QUIZ 33 _____   *Algebra 1*

Sections 8.9–8.11
(–8 each)

Write the reciprocal of each.

_____$\frac{3}{2}$_____   **1.** $\frac{2}{3}$

_____$\frac{1}{4}$_____   **2.** 4

_____$\frac{1}{xy}$_____   **3.** xy

_____$\frac{b-y}{a-x}$_____   **4.** $\frac{a-x}{b-y}$

Multiply.

_____$\frac{6b^2}{5a^2c}$_____   **5.** $\frac{4ab}{10c^2} \cdot \frac{3bc}{a^3}$

_____$\frac{x-1}{x+7}$_____   **6.** $\frac{x^2+3x+2}{x^2-3x-10} \cdot \frac{x^2-6x+5}{x^2+8x+7}$

Divide.

_____$\frac{ax}{4bm}$_____   **7.** $\frac{5mn}{6bx} \div \frac{10m^2n}{3ax^2}$

_____$\frac{3m}{7x}$_____   **8.** $\frac{3abm}{7} \div abx$

_____$10a$_____   **9.** $(4a+2) \div \frac{2a+1}{5a}$

_____$\frac{3c}{2b}$_____   **10.** $\frac{\frac{2b}{3c}}{\frac{4b^2}{9c^2}}$

TEST 7   *Algebra 1*

DIRECTIONS: Show all of your work neatly in pencil in the space provided. Copy your answers from your work space into the space provided for the answer. Use another sheet to keep all work and answers covered at all times.

Reduce to lowest terms.

$\dfrac{y}{a}$ **1.** $\dfrac{a^2xy^2}{a^3xy}$

$\dfrac{2nx^2}{5amyz}$ **2.** $\dfrac{16m^2nx^2z^2}{40am^3yz^3}$

$\dfrac{-a}{6bd}$ **3.** $\dfrac{-7a^2bcd^3}{42ab^2cd^4}$

$\dfrac{1}{2x-3a}$ **4.** $\dfrac{2x}{4x^2-6ax}$

$\dfrac{x+1}{x-4}$ **5.** $\dfrac{x^2-6x-7}{x^2-11x+28}$

$\dfrac{1}{4a-7}$ **6.** $\dfrac{4a+7}{16a^2-49}$

Change to an integral or mixed expression.

$4a+1$ **7.** $\dfrac{36ac+9c}{9c}$

$2x^2-4x+1-\dfrac{1}{2x}$ **8.** $\dfrac{4x^3-8x^2+2x-1}{2x}$

Perform the addition or subtraction indicated.

$\dfrac{19x}{10}$ **9.** $\dfrac{2x}{5}+\dfrac{3x}{2}$

$\dfrac{m}{2}$ **10.** $\dfrac{4m}{3}-\dfrac{5m}{6}$

$\dfrac{3x + 34}{12}$ **11.** $\dfrac{2x + 1}{3} + \dfrac{x - 2}{4} - \dfrac{x - 3}{6} + \dfrac{5 - x}{2}$

$\dfrac{a^2 - 2x^2}{a - x}$ **12.** $a + x - \dfrac{x^2}{a - x}$

$\dfrac{6x - 4}{(x + 2)(x - 2)}$ **13.** $\dfrac{x}{x - 2} - \dfrac{x - 2}{x + 2}$

$\dfrac{12x - 19}{(x - 2)(x - 3)}$ **14.** $\dfrac{12}{x - 3} + \dfrac{5}{x^2 - 5x + 6}$

Multiply.

$\dfrac{b}{2ax}$ **15.** $\dfrac{3ab}{4xy} \cdot \dfrac{2y}{3a^2}$

$\dfrac{5bn}{4my}$ **16.** $\dfrac{4mn}{3xy} \cdot \dfrac{15bx}{16m^2}$

$\dfrac{3}{a - c}$ **17.** $\dfrac{a + c}{2} \cdot \dfrac{6}{a^2 - c^2}$

$\dfrac{4xy + 4y}{x - 1}$ or $\dfrac{4y(x + 1)}{x - 1}$ **18.** $\dfrac{x^2 + 2x + 1}{y} \cdot \dfrac{4y^2}{x^2 - 1}$

$\dfrac{x - 1}{x + 7}$ **19.** $\dfrac{x^2 + 3x + 2}{x^2 - 3x - 10} \cdot \dfrac{x^2 - 6x + 5}{x^2 + 8x + 7}$

Name _____ Date _____ Score _____

QUIZ 34

Sections 8.9–8.13
(–8 each)

Divide.

$\dfrac{y}{2}$ _____ 1. $\dfrac{x^2}{y} \div \dfrac{2x^2}{y^2}$

$\dfrac{7b^2}{15c}$ _____ 2. $\dfrac{6c}{5b} \div \dfrac{18c^2}{7b^3}$

$\dfrac{5(x-y)}{2}$ or $\dfrac{5x-5y}{2}$ _____ 3. $\dfrac{x^2-y^2}{2a} \div \dfrac{x+y}{5a}$ $\qquad \dfrac{x^2-y^2}{2a} \cdot \dfrac{5a}{x+y} = \dfrac{(x+y)(x-y)}{2 \cdot a} \cdot \dfrac{5a}{x+y} = \dfrac{5(x-y)}{2}$

$\dfrac{x}{y}$ _____ 4. $\dfrac{\frac{x^2}{y^2}}{\frac{x}{y}}$ $\qquad\qquad\qquad\qquad\qquad\qquad\qquad\qquad$ or

$\qquad \dfrac{5x-5y}{2}$

Solve for *x*.

$x = 5$ _____ 5. $\dfrac{x}{2} + \dfrac{x}{6} = \dfrac{10}{3}$

$x = 5$ _____ 6. $2x + \dfrac{x}{3} = \dfrac{35}{3}$

$x = 1$ _____ 7. $\dfrac{3x}{4} + \dfrac{7x}{16} - \dfrac{x}{2} - \dfrac{9x}{16} = \dfrac{1}{8}$

Write the reciprocal of each.

$\dfrac{3}{2}$ _____ 8. $\dfrac{2}{3}$

$\dfrac{1}{x+y}$ _____ 9. $x + y$

4 _____ 10. $\dfrac{1}{4}$

91

QUIZ 35 *Algebra 1*

Sections 8.9–8.13 and
Algebraic Representation Exercises
(–8 each)

Find each answer.

_____$\frac{y}{x}$_____ **1.** Multiply: $\frac{12x}{5y} \cdot \frac{15y^2}{36x^2}$

_____$\frac{1}{4}$_____ **2.** Divide: $\frac{3r^2}{9r^3} \div \frac{8r^4}{6r^5}$

Solve each equation.

_____$y = 48$_____ **3.** $\frac{y}{3} + \frac{y}{2} = 40$

_____$c = 24$_____ **4.** $\frac{5c}{8} - \frac{c}{3} = \frac{5c}{6} - 13$

_____$a = 2$_____ **5.** $\frac{3}{a} = \frac{19}{3a} - \frac{5}{3}$

_____$m = 2$_____ **6.** $\frac{2}{m} = \frac{5}{3m - 1}$

Solve the word problem.

_____70 mph; 170 mph_____ **7.** A passenger train travels 100 mph faster than a car. In the time it takes the car to travel 140 miles, the train can travel 340 miles. Find the speed of each.

$\frac{140}{x} = \frac{340}{x + 100}$

$x = $ speed of car $\qquad 140(x + 100) = 340x$
$x + 100 = $ speed of train $\qquad 140x + 14{,}000 = 340x$
$\qquad\qquad\qquad\qquad\qquad 200x = 14{,}000$
$\qquad\qquad\qquad\qquad\qquad x = 70$

Represent algebraically.

_____$\frac{x}{a + b}$_____ **8.** Indicate what part x is of $a + b$.

$x + 100 = 170$

_____$a\left(\frac{x + y}{3}\right)$_____ **9.** Indicate the sum of x and y divided by 3 and that result multiplied by a.

_____$\frac{a + x}{b + x}$_____ **10.** Indicate the result when x is added to both the numerator and denominator of $\frac{a}{b}$.

QUIZ 36 _____ *Algebra 1*

Section 9.1
(−6 each)

Write as a ratio in the form of a fraction. Express each ratio in simplest form. Simplest form includes having no fractions or decimals as terms in the ratio.

$\dfrac{2}{1}$ _____ **1.** $14 to $7

$\dfrac{5}{36}$ _____ **2.** 5 inches to 1 yard

$\dfrac{3}{7}$ _____ **3.** 3 days to 1 week

$\dfrac{1}{4}$ _____ **4.** 25¢ to $1.00

$\dfrac{5}{6}$ _____ **5.** 10 days to 12 days

$\dfrac{1}{2}$ _____ **6.** 2 quarts to 1 gallon

$\dfrac{1}{4}$ _____ **7.** 4:16

$\dfrac{1}{2}$ _____ **8.** 19:38

$\dfrac{26}{5}$ _____ **9.** 5.2:1

$\dfrac{1}{2}$ _____ **10.** 3:6

$\dfrac{7}{1}$ _____ **11.** 210:30

$\dfrac{1}{24}$ _____ **12.** $\frac{1}{8}$ to 3

$\dfrac{40}{7}$ _____ **13.** 4 to .7

$\dfrac{8}{13}$ _____ **14.** $\dfrac{1.6}{2.6}$

$\dfrac{9}{20}$ _____ **15.** $2\frac{1}{4}$ to 5

QUIZ 37   *Algebra 1*

Section 9.2
(–8 each)

Follow the directions.

_____3 and x_____   **1.** Name the means in $2:3 = x:5$.

_____a and d_____   **2.** Name the extremes in $\frac{a}{b} = \frac{c}{d}$.

_____± 9_____   **3.** Find the mean proportional between 3 and 27.

$$\frac{3}{x} = \frac{x}{27}$$
$$x^2 = 81$$
$$x = \pm 9$$

Find the value of *x.*

_____$x = 6$_____   **4.** $\frac{2}{3} = \frac{4}{x}$

_____$x = \frac{15}{4}$_____   **5.** $\frac{5}{x} = \frac{4}{3}$

_____$x = 3$_____   **6.** $\frac{x + 2}{x} = \frac{10}{6}$

_____$x = 5$_____   **7.** $\frac{x}{x - 1} = \frac{15}{12}$

Reduce these ratios.

_____$\frac{a + b}{a - b}$_____   **8.** $\frac{a^2 - b^2}{(a - b)^2}$

_____$\frac{3}{1}$_____   **9.** $\frac{\frac{3}{4}}{\frac{1}{4}}$

Solve the word problem.

_____150 feet_____   **10.** The ratio of the height of two buildings is 7:5. The first building is 210 feet tall. How tall is the second building?

$$\frac{7}{5} = \frac{210}{x}$$
$$7x = 1,050$$
$$x = 150$$

QUIZ 38 _____ *Algebra 1*

Sections 9.5–9.7
(–8 each)

Tell if the circled part is a *constant, dependent variable*, or *independent variable*.

independent variable **1.** $C = 2\pi\textcircled{r}$

dependent variable **2.** $\textcircled{C} = 2\pi r$

constant **3.** $C = 2\textcircled{$\pi$}r$

Give the corresponding angle for angle A in the similar triangles.

∠X **4.**

∠Z **5.**

Follow the directions.

$\frac{2}{1}$ **6.** Give the ratio of $12x$ to $6x$.

$\frac{2}{x}$ **7.** Give the ratio of $\frac{4}{5}x$ to $\frac{2}{5}x^2$.

$\frac{4}{9}$ **8.** Choose the greater ratio: $\frac{4}{9}$ or $\frac{2}{5}$.

175 **9.** In the formula $\frac{p}{p'} = \frac{a}{a'}$, find p' when $p = 105$, $a = 3$, and $a' = 5$.

324 square feet **10.** In the formula $\frac{A}{A'} = \frac{a^2}{a'^2}$, find A' when $A = 81$ square feet, $a = 21$ feet, and $a' = 42$ feet.

99

TEST 8 _____ *Algebra 1*

DIRECTIONS: Show all of your work neatly in pencil in the space provided. Copy your answers from your work space into the space provided for the answer. Use another sheet to keep all work and answers covered at all times.

Divide the fractions.

_____ $\dfrac{ax}{4bm}$ _____ **1.** $\dfrac{5mn}{6bx} \div \dfrac{10m^2n}{3ax^2}$

_____ $10a$ _____ **2.** $(4a + 2) \div \dfrac{2a + 1}{5a}$

_____ $\dfrac{4m}{49}$ _____ **3.** $\dfrac{\frac{4}{7}}{\frac{7}{m}}$

_____ $\dfrac{3c}{2b}$ _____ **4.** $\dfrac{\frac{2b}{3c}}{\frac{4b^2}{9c^2}}$

Clear each equation of fractions and solve for *x*.

_____ $x = 5$ _____ **5.** $\dfrac{x}{2} + \dfrac{x}{6} = \dfrac{10}{3}$

_____ $x = 3$ _____ **6.** $\dfrac{25x}{18} - \dfrac{5x}{9} + \dfrac{2x}{3} - \dfrac{5x}{6} = 2$

_____ $x = 1$ _____ **7.** $\dfrac{3x}{4} + \dfrac{7x}{16} - \dfrac{x}{2} - \dfrac{9x}{16} = \dfrac{1}{8}$

_____ $x = 17$ _____ **8.** $\dfrac{x - 2}{x + 3} = \dfrac{3}{4}$

_____ $x = 1$ _____ **9.** $\dfrac{4}{x + 2} + \dfrac{7}{x + 3} = \dfrac{37}{(x + 2)(x + 3)}$

RATIO AND PROPORTION: Answer each question.

$\dfrac{1}{2}$ **10.** What is the ratio of $4m$ to $8m$?

$\dfrac{3}{5}$ **11.** Which is greater, $\dfrac{5}{9}$ or $\dfrac{3}{5}$?

$\dfrac{3}{1}$ **12.** What is the ratio of 21 days to 1 week?

$x = 6$ **13.** $\dfrac{2}{3} = \dfrac{4}{x}$

$x = 3$ **14.** $\dfrac{10}{6} = \dfrac{x+2}{x}$

$x = -4$ **15.** $\dfrac{3}{1} = \dfrac{x-2}{x+2}$

150 feet   **16.** The ratios of the height of two trees is 7:5. If the first tree is 210 feet high, how tall is the second tree?

$P' = 315$ yards   **17.** The perimeters of two similar polygons have the same ratio as any two corresponding sides. This can be expressed by the formula: $\dfrac{P}{P'} = \dfrac{a}{a'}$. Find P' when $P = 210$ yards, $a = 2$, and $a' = 3$.

Name _____

Provide the answer requested.

$\dfrac{b}{a}$ **18.** What is the reciprocal of $\frac{a}{b}$?

$\dfrac{bc}{2a^2}$ **19.** What is the reciprocal of $\frac{2a^2}{bc}$?

$\dfrac{1}{rs}$ **20.** What is the reciprocal of rs?

$\left(\dfrac{a+m}{2}\right)n$ **21.** Write an algebraic expression to indicate the sum of a and m divided by 2 and the result multiplied by n.

$\dfrac{a+b}{c-b}$ **22.** Indicate the result when b is added to the numerator and subtracted from the denominator of the fraction $\frac{a}{c}$.

32, 24   **23.** Divide 56 into two parts such that $\frac{3}{8}$ of the larger number decreased by 6 equals $\frac{1}{4}$ of the smaller number. (Show your work.)

QUIZ 39 _____ *Algebra 1*

Section 10.1
(–10 each)

Solve for *x*.

_____ $x = 12$ _____   **1.** $9x = 108$

_____ $x = 6$ _____   **2.** $\frac{3}{5}x = 3.6$

_____ $x = 4$ _____   **3.** $5x - 4 = 16$

_____ $x = 16$ _____   **4.** $\frac{3}{8}x + 7 = 13$

_____ $x = 2$ _____   **5.** $19 + x = 21$

_____ $x = -6$ _____   **6.** $9x + 7 = 7x - 5$

_____ $x = 6$ _____   **7.** $2x - \frac{x}{6} = 11$

_____ $x = 12$ _____   **8.** $\frac{4}{7} = \frac{8}{x + 2}$

_____ $x = 22$ _____   **9.** $3x - (2x + 7) = 15$

Name _____ Date _____ Score _____

QUIZ 40   *Algebra 1*

Solve for x.

_____$x = b - a$_____   **1.** $x + a = b$

_____$x = a + 6$_____   **2.** $x - 6 = a$

_____$x = \dfrac{y}{a}$_____   **3.** $ax = y$

_____$x = \dfrac{m + n}{b}$_____   **4.** $bx = m + n$

_____$x = 1$_____   **5.** $abx = ab$

_____$x = \dfrac{y - c}{b}$_____   **6.** $bx + c = y$

_____$x = \dfrac{b + y}{4b}$_____   **7.** $4bx = b + y$

_____$x = \dfrac{ab}{a + b}$_____   **8.** $(a + b)x = ab$

Follow the directions.

_____$d = \dfrac{spc^2}{t}$_____   **9.** In the formula $t = \dfrac{spc^2}{d}$, solve for d.

_____$r = \dfrac{E - IR}{I}$ or $\dfrac{E}{I} - R$_____   **10.** In the formula $I = \dfrac{E}{R + r}$, solve for r.

QUIZ 41 _____ *Algebra 1*

Sections 11.1–11.2
(–8 each)

Tell the quadrant in which each point is located. If the point is on an axis, write *none*.

_____II_____	**1.** (–3,2)
_____I_____	**2.** (5,4)
_____III_____	**3.** (–7,–2)
_____IV_____	**4.** (6,–4)
_____none_____	**5.** (0,8)

Answer the questions.

_____–4_____	**6.** In the coordinates (5,–4), which number represents the *y* value?
_____(0,0)_____	**7.** What are the coordinates of the origin?

Find the coordinates of the *x* and *y* intercepts of the equation.

x-intercept (4,0)	**8.** $x + 2y = 4$
y-intercept (0,2)	**9.**
x-intercept (3,0)	**10.** $6x - 2y = 18$
y-intercept (0,–9)	**11.**

QUIZ 42 *Algebra 1*

Write *yes* if independent; write *no* if not.

_____yes_____   **1.** $x - y = 3$
$y + x = 4$

_____no_____   **2.** $2x + 2y = 8$
$x + y = 4$

_____yes_____   **3.** $x - y = 1$
$x + y = 1$

Write *true* or *false*.

_____true_____   **4.** Graphing can be used to solve a system of equations.

_____false_____   **5.** All systems of equations have a solution.

_____true_____   **6.** Some systems have infinite solutions.

_____false_____   **7.** Lines that coincide are inconsistent.

_____false_____   **8.** Lines that are parallel are dependent.

_____true_____   **9.** The point of intersection is the solution.

Use your graph paper to solve graphically if possible.

___$x = 8$ $y = 0$___   **10.** $x + y = 8$
$x - y = 8$

___$x = 0$ $y = 6$___   **11.** $2x + y = 6$
$y = 4x + 6$

QUIZ 43   *Algebra 1*

Sections 11.2–11.7
(–7 each)

Find the *x*-intercept.

_____(20,0)_____   **1.** $x + 5y = 20$

_____(9,0)_____   **2.** $3x - 2y = 27$

Find the *y*-intercept.

_____(0,8)_____   **3.** $y - 2x = 8$

_____(0,7)_____   **4.** $21 - 3y = 7x$

Solve by the addition method.

_____$x = 5$_____   **5.** $\begin{cases} x + y = 4 \\ x - y = 6 \end{cases}$
_____$y = -1$_____   **6.**

_____$x = 3$_____   **7.** $\begin{cases} 2x - y = 9 \\ 3x + y = 6 \end{cases}$
_____$y = -3$_____   **8.**

Solve by the substitution method.

_____$x = 3$_____   **9.** $\begin{cases} y = x - 4 \\ y = -2x + 5 \end{cases}$
_____$y = -1$_____   **10.**

_____$x = 2$_____   **11.** $\begin{cases} x + 4y = -10 \\ 2x - y = 7 \end{cases}$
_____$y = -3$_____   **12.**

113

TEST 9 (Nine-Weeks Exam) _____ *Algebra 1*

Units 8–11
(–5 each)

DIRECTIONS: Show all of your work neatly in pencil in the space provided. Copy your answers from your work space into the space provided for the answer. Use another sheet to keep all work and answers covered at all times.

FRACTIONS: Perform the operation indicated.

$\dfrac{a-5b}{6}$ _____ **1.** $\dfrac{a-b}{2} - \dfrac{a+b}{3}$

$\dfrac{1}{b-1}$ _____ **2.** $\dfrac{b+c}{b^2-1} \cdot \dfrac{b+1}{b+c}$

$\dfrac{a-3}{a+3}$ _____ **3.** $\dfrac{a-3}{a+7} \div \dfrac{a^2-9}{a^2+4a-21}$

Clear each equation of fractions and solve for *x*.

_____ $x=15$ _____ **4.** $\dfrac{x}{2} + \dfrac{x}{3} - \dfrac{x}{4} + \dfrac{3x}{10} - \dfrac{5x}{12} = 7$

_____ $x=17$ _____ **5.** $\dfrac{x-2}{x+3} = \dfrac{3}{4}$

_____ 1,000 pounds _____ **6.** How many pounds of iron are produced from 4,200 pounds of iron ore if the ratio of iron to iron ore is $\dfrac{5}{21}$?

_____ 161 cu. in. _____ **7.** Using the formula $\dfrac{V}{V'} = \dfrac{h}{h'}$, find V when $h = 1$, $h' = 6$, and $V' = 966$ cu. in.

LITERAL EQUATIONS: Solve for the variable indicated.

_____ $g = \dfrac{2s}{t^2}$ _____ **8.** Solve for g when $s = \frac{1}{2}gt^2$.

_____ $w = \dfrac{V}{lh}$ _____ **9.** Solve for w when $V = lwh$.

SYSTEMS OF EQUATIONS: Solve the equations graphically if possible.

_____(−6,0)_____   **10.** $\begin{cases} x + 3y = -6 \\ 2x - 4y = -12 \end{cases}$

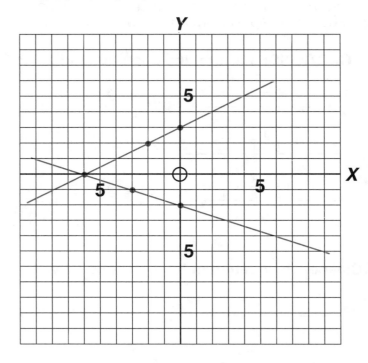

_____inconsistent_____   **11.** $\begin{cases} x = 4 + y \\ y = 3 + x \end{cases}$

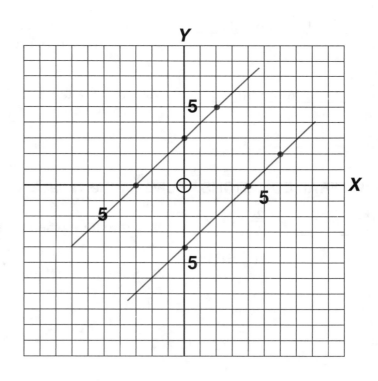

Graphing. Provide the answer requested.

_____IV_____   **12.** In which quadrant are the coordinates $(5, -3)$ located?

_____III_____   **13.** In which quadrant are the coordinates $(-8, -4)$ located?

_____none_____   **14.** In which quadrant are the coordinates $(7, 0)$ located?

___(3,0); (0,2)___   **15.** Write the coordinates for the x and y intercepts of the equation $2x + 3y = 6$.

SYSTEMS OF EQUATIONS: Solve by elimination by addition.

_____(11,5)_____   **16.** $\begin{cases} 7x - 5y = 52 \\ 2x + 5y = 47 \end{cases}$

_____(8,3)_____   **17.** $\begin{cases} 6x - 5y = 33 \\ 4x + 4y = 44 \end{cases}$

Solve by elimination by substitution.

_____(10,6)_____   **18.** $\begin{cases} x - y = 4 \\ 4y - x = 14 \end{cases}$

QUIZ 44 *Algebra 1*

Sections 11.1–11.8
(–10 each)

Tell the quadrant in which each point is located. If the point is on an axis, write *none*.

_____III_____ **1.** (–5,–3)

_____IV_____ **2.** (7,–2)

_____none_____ **3.** (0,8)

Answer each question.

indeterminate
or dependent **4.** If two lines coincide, they are said to be __?__.

inconsistent **5.** If two lines are parallel, they are said to be __?__.

_(10,0), (0,15)_ **6.** What are the coordinates for the x and y intercepts for the equation $3x + 2y = 30$?

Solve by using the elimination by addition method.

_____(–9,25)_____ **7.** $\begin{cases} 3x + 2y = 23 \\ x + y = 16 \end{cases}$

_____(–6,9)_____ **8.** $\begin{cases} 2x + 3y = 15 \\ 3x + 2y = 0 \end{cases}$

QUIZ 45 _____ *Algebra 1*

Section 11.9
(–8 each)

Give what each equation must be multiplied by to eliminate the term containing *x*.

_____ b _____   **1.** $\begin{cases} ax + by = r \\ \\ -bx + cy = s \end{cases}$

_____ a _____   **2.**

_____ b _____   **3.** $\begin{cases} mx - ny = z \\ \\ bx - ny = r \end{cases}$

_____ $-m$ _____   **4.**

_____ c _____   **5.** $\begin{cases} ax - by = m \\ \\ cx - dy = r \end{cases}$

_____ $-a$ _____   **6.**

Solve for *x* and *y*.

_____ $x = \frac{cr - bs}{ac - ab}$ _____   **7.** $\begin{cases} ax + by = r \\ \\ ax + cy = s \end{cases}$

_____ $y = \frac{r - s}{b - c}$ _____   **8.**

_____ $x = \frac{ms + nr}{cs + dr}$ _____   **9.** $\begin{cases} cx + ry = m \\ \\ dx - sy = n \end{cases}$

_____ $y = \frac{dm - cn}{dr + cs}$ _____   **10.**

Name _____   Date _____   Score _____

QUIZ 46   *Algebra 1*

Raise to the power indicated.

_____$25x^{10}y^4$_____   **1.** $(5x^5y^2)^2$

_____$-27x^6y\textcircled{5}$_____   **2.** $(-3x^2y^5)^3$

_____$\dfrac{16x^8}{81y^4}$_____   **3.** $\left(\dfrac{-2x^2}{3y}\right)^4$

_____$\dfrac{a^{2n}b^{2n}}{x^n y^{3n}}$_____   **4.** $\left(\dfrac{a^2b^2}{xy^3}\right)^n$

_____$25m^4 - 60m^2 + 36$_____   **5.** $(5m^2 - 6)^2$

_____$a^2 + b^2 + c^2 + 2ab - 2ac - 2bc$_____   **6.** $(a + b - c)^2$

_____$9a^2 + 4b^2 + 16c^2 + 12ab - 24ac - 16bc$_____   **7.** $(3a + 2b - 4c)^2$

_____$x^3 + 3x^2y + 3xy^2 + y^3$_____   **8.** $(x + y)^3$

Solve the word problem.

_____student—125_____   **9.** Two hundred tickets were sold for the concert for a total income of $475. Student

_____adult—75_____   **10.** tickets sold for $2.00 each and adult tickets for $3.00 each. How many tickets of each kind were sold?

$$x + y = 200 \qquad\qquad -3x - 3y = -600$$
$$2x + 3y = 475 \qquad\qquad \underline{2x + 3y = 475}$$
$$\qquad\qquad\qquad\qquad\qquad -x \qquad\qquad -125$$

$$x = 125$$
$$(200 - x) = 75$$

QUIZ 47   *Algebra 1*

Sections 12.4–12.6
(–8 each)

Raise to the power indicated.

$27a^6b^9$ **1.** $(3a^2b^3)^3$

$-32x^{10}y^{25}$ **2.** $(-2x^2y^5)^5$

$\dfrac{4}{9a^6}$ **3.** $\left(\dfrac{-2}{3a^3}\right)^2$

$\dfrac{6^n a^{2n}}{5^n b^{3n}}$ **4.** $\left(\dfrac{6a^2}{5b^3}\right)^n$

Find the root indicated.

$2ab^5$ **5.** $\sqrt[3]{8a^3b^{15}}$

$2x^2y^3$ **6.** $\sqrt[4]{16x^8y^{12}}$

$\dfrac{9x^3y^2}{11a^2bz^5}$ **7.** $\sqrt{\dfrac{81x^6y^4}{121a^4b^2z^{10}}}$

$\dfrac{(a-b)^2}{2a^2}$ **8.** $\sqrt[6]{\dfrac{(a-b)^{12}}{64a^{12}}}$

35 **9.** $\sqrt{1,225}$

21 **10.** $\sqrt{441}$

QUIZ 48 _____ *Algebra 1*

Find the square root.

_____$x + 3$_____   **1.** $x^2 + 6x + 9$

_____$3x - 1$_____   **2.** $9x^2 - 6x + 1$

_____$\dfrac{3x}{y} + \dfrac{3y}{x}$_____   **3.** $\dfrac{9x^2}{y^2} + 18 + \dfrac{9y^2}{x^2}$

_____$2x + 3$_____   **4.** $4x^2 + 12x + 9$

_____99_____   **5.** $9{,}801$

_____$\dfrac{19}{31}$_____   **6.** $\dfrac{361}{961}$

Give the square root and cube root.

_____square root: 8_____   **7.** 64

_____cube root: 4_____   **8.**

_____square root: 27_____   **9.** 729

_____cube root: 9_____   **10.**

square root

$\sqrt{729}$ $\;\textcircled{27}\;$ $\sqrt[3]{729} = \sqrt[3]{27 \cdot 27}$

$\begin{array}{r} \overline{729} \\ -4 \\ \hline 329 \\ \underline{329} \end{array}$ $\quad 47$

$= \sqrt[3]{3 \cdot 9 \cdot 3 \cdot 9}$

$= \sqrt[3]{3 \cdot 3 \cdot 3 \cdot 3 \cdot 3 \cdot 3}$

$= 3 \cdot 3$

$= 9$

TEST 10 _____ *Algebra 1*

Units 11–12 (Sections 11.8–12.9)
(–4 each)

DIRECTIONS: Show all of your work neatly in pencil in the space provided. Copy your answers from your work space into the space provided for the answer. Use another sheet to keep all work and answers covered at all times.

Raise to the power indicated.

_____$a^4b^4c^6$_____ **1.** $(a^2b^2c^3)^2$

_____$8a^6c^3$_____ **2.** $(2a^2c)^3$

_____$-8x^6y^3$_____ **3.** $(-2x^2y)^3$

_____$81x^{12}y^8$_____ **4.** $(-3x^3y^2)^4$

_____$\dfrac{25}{a^2b^2}$_____ **5.** $\left(-\dfrac{5}{ab}\right)^2$

_____$-\dfrac{27x^3}{8y^3}$_____ **6.** $\left(-\dfrac{3x}{2y}\right)^3$

_____$\dfrac{a^{4n}b^{6n}}{x^{2n}y^{8n}}$_____ **7.** $\left(\dfrac{a^2b^3}{xy^4}\right)^{2n}$

_____$9x^2 + 24xy + 16y^2$_____ **8.** $(3x + 4y)^2$

_____$a^2 + b^2 + c^2 + 2ab + 2ac + 2bc$_____ **9.** $(a + b + c)^2$

_____$25a^2 + 4c^2 + 4b^2 - 20ac - 20ab + 8bc$_____ **10.** $(5a - 2c - 2b)^2$

_____$x^3 + 3x^2y + 3xy^2 + y^3$_____ **11.** $(x + y)^3$

Find the indicated roots.

_____ ab^2c^3 _____   **12.** $\sqrt[3]{a^3b^6c^9}$

_____ a^2xy^3 _____   **13.** $\sqrt[5]{a^{10}x^5y^{15}}$

_____ $-2a^2b^5$ _____   **14.** $\sqrt[3]{-8a^6b^{15}}$

_____ $3p^3r$ _____   **15.** $-\sqrt[3]{-27p^9r^3}$

_____ $\dfrac{-2x^3b^2}{3mn^4}$ _____   **16.** $\sqrt[3]{\dfrac{-8x^9b^6}{27m^3n^{12}}}$

Find the square root.

_____ $c - 6$ _____   **17.** $c^2 - 12c + 36$

_____ $\dfrac{2a}{b} + \dfrac{2b}{a}$ _____   **18.** $\dfrac{4a^2}{b^2} + 8 + \dfrac{4b^2}{a^2}$

_____ $x + 2y + 3z$ _____   **19.** $x^2 + 4xy + 4y^2 + 6xz + 12yz + 9z^2$

Solve for *x* and *y*.

$x = \dfrac{am + bc}{a^2 + b^2}$ $y = \dfrac{bm - ac}{a^2 + b^2}$ **20.** $\begin{cases} ax + by = m \\ bx - ay = c \end{cases}$

Write a system of equations for the following problems and solve.

$\begin{cases} x + 5y = 86 \\ x + y = 38 \end{cases}$

number of $1 bills = 26
number of $5 bills = 12

21. An errand boy went to the bank to deposit some bills for his employer. Some were one-dollar bills and the rest were five-dollar bills. The total value of the bills was $86 and the number of bills was 38. Find the number of each kind of bill.

$\begin{cases} 2.50x + 1.50y = 650 \\ x + y = 300 \end{cases}$

200 adults; 100 students

22. The receipts from 300 tickets for a high school program were $650. Adults were charged $2.50 each and students $1.50. How many tickets of each kind were sold?

QUIZ 49 *Algebra 1*

Section 13.1
(–7 each)

Find each answer.

1	**1.** $5^0 =$
$\frac{1}{4}$	**2.** $2^{-2} =$
4	**3.** $\left(-\frac{1}{2}\right)^{-2} =$
a	**4.** $a^3(a^{-2}) =$
x	**5.** $(x^{\frac{1}{2}})(x^{\frac{1}{2}}) =$
$\frac{1}{x}$	**6.** $\frac{x^5}{x^6}$
x^8	**7.** $x^4 \div x^{-4}$

Write with positive exponents.

$\frac{5}{x^2}$	**8.** $5x^{-2}$
$\frac{c^3}{bd^3}$	**9.** $b^{-1}c^3d^{-3}$

Solve.

$x = 27$	**10.** $x^{\frac{1}{3}} = 3$
$x = 25$	**11.** $x^{\frac{1}{2}} = 5$

Write without a denominator.

$cdn^{-1}x^{-1}$	**12.** $\frac{cd}{nx}$
$ab^{-1}y^2$	**13.** $\frac{a}{by^{-2}}$

QUIZ 50 *Algebra 1*

Sections 13.2–13.4
(–8 each)

Answer the questions about $\sqrt[3]{7^4}$.

_____7 or 7^4_____   **1.** What is the radicand?

_____4_____   **2.** What is the power?

_____3_____   **3.** What is the index?

Answer the questions about $\sqrt{x}$.

_____x_____   **4.** What is the radicand?

_____1_____   **5.** What is the power?

_____2_____   **6.** What is the index?

Tell if *rational* or *irrational*.

_____irrational_____   **7.** $\sqrt{17}$

_____rational_____   **8.** $\sqrt{25}$

_____rational_____   **9.** $\sqrt{100}$

_____irrational_____   **10.** $\sqrt{5}$

Name _____ Date _____ Score _____

QUIZ 51 _Algebra 1_

Sections 13.5–13.7
(–8 each)

Reduce.

_____4_____   **1.** $\sqrt{16}$

_____$3\sqrt{2}$_____   **2.** $\sqrt{18}$

_____$2\sqrt[3]{3}$_____   **3.** $\sqrt[3]{24}$

_____$5a\sqrt{2a}$_____   **4.** $\sqrt{50a^3}$

____$2yz^2\sqrt[3]{2x^2y^2z}$____   **5.** $\sqrt[3]{16x^2y^5z^7}$

_____$2x^3\sqrt{5x}$_____   **6.** $\sqrt{20x^7}$

___$\frac{\sqrt{3}}{3}$ or $\frac{1}{3}\sqrt{3}$___   **7.** $\sqrt{\frac{1}{3}}$

___$\frac{\sqrt{6}}{4}$ or $\frac{1}{4}\sqrt{6}$___   **8.** $\sqrt{\frac{3}{8}}$

_____$\frac{\sqrt{3x}}{x}$_____   **9.** $\sqrt{\frac{3}{x}}$

__$\frac{\sqrt[3]{6}}{2}$ or $\frac{1}{2}\sqrt[3]{6}$__   **10.** $\sqrt[3]{\frac{3}{4}}$

QUIZ 52

Write if *rational* or *irrational*.

___rational___   **1.** $\sqrt{4}$

___irrational___   **2.** $\sqrt{5}$

___irrational___   **3.** $\sqrt[3]{4}$

___rational___   **4.** $\sqrt[3]{8}$

Reduce.

___$2\sqrt{2}$___   **5.** $\sqrt{8}$

___$3\sqrt{5}$___   **6.** $\sqrt{45}$

___$5\sqrt{2}$___   **7.** $\sqrt{50}$

___$3\sqrt[3]{3}$___   **8.** $\sqrt[3]{81}$

Reduce to the same order.

___$\sqrt[4]{4}$___   **9.** $\sqrt{2}$, $\sqrt[4]{3}$

___$\sqrt[4]{3}$___   **10.**

___$\sqrt[6]{125}$___   **11.** $\sqrt{5}$, $\sqrt[3]{6}$

___$\sqrt[6]{36}$___   **12.**

QUIZ 53 _____ *Algebra 1*

Answer the questions about $5\sqrt[3]{7^2}$.

_____7 or 7^2_____	**1.** What is the radicand?
_____3_____	**2.** What is the index?
_____5_____	**3.** What is the coefficient?
_____2_____	**4.** What is the power?

Reduce.

_____$5\sqrt{2}$_____	**5.** $\sqrt{50}$
_____$\frac{\sqrt{2}}{2}$ or $\frac{1}{2}\sqrt{2}$_____	**6.** $\sqrt{\frac{1}{2}}$
_____$4\sqrt{2}$_____	**7.** $2\sqrt{8}$

Add.

_____$13\sqrt{3}$_____	**8.** $8\sqrt{3} + 5\sqrt{3}$
_____$13\sqrt{2}$_____	**9.** $\sqrt{98} + \sqrt{72}$

Multiply.

_____3_____	**10.** $\sqrt{3} \cdot \sqrt{3}$
_____$2\sqrt{33}$_____	**11.** $2\sqrt{11} \cdot \sqrt{3}$
_____48_____	**12.** $4\sqrt{2} \cdot 3\sqrt{8}$

TEST 11   *Algebra 1*

DIRECTIONS: Show all of your work neatly in pencil in the space provided. Copy your answers from your work space into the space provided for the answer. Use another sheet to keep all work and answers covered at all times.

Write with positive exponents.

$\dfrac{2}{x}$ _____ **1.** $2x^{-1}$

$\dfrac{1}{x^3 y^2}$ _____ **2.** $x^{-3} y^{-2}$

ab _____ **3.** $\dfrac{1}{a^{-1} b^{-1}}$

$\dfrac{bx}{ay}$ _____ **4.** $\dfrac{a^{-1} x}{b^{-1} y}$

Write without a denominator.

$a^2 b^{-2}$ _____ **5.** $\dfrac{1}{a^{-2} b^2}$

$ab^{-1} x y^{-1}$ _____ **6.** $\dfrac{ax}{by}$

SIMPLIFY: Write the value of each term.

1 _____ **7.** $(a^2 b^4 c)^0$

16 _____ **8.** $64^{\frac{2}{3}}$

Express without a radical and with positive fractional exponents.

$a^{\frac{1}{2}} b^{\frac{3}{2}}$ _____ **9.** $\sqrt{ab^3}$

$\dfrac{5}{x^{\frac{1}{2}} y^{\frac{1}{2}}}$ _____ **10.** $5\sqrt{x^{-1} y^{-1}}$

Express with radical signs and with positive exponents.

$\sqrt[5]{a^2}$	**11.** $a^{\frac{2}{5}}$
$\sqrt[3]{ab^2}$	**12.** $a^{\frac{1}{3}}b^{\frac{2}{3}}$
$\sqrt[4]{\dfrac{a}{b^3}}$	**13.** $a^{\frac{1}{4}}b^{-\frac{3}{4}}$

Multiply.

a	**14.** $a^3 \cdot a^{-2}$
1	**15.** $a^4 \cdot a^{-4}$
x^3	**16.** $x^{\frac{1}{2}} \cdot x^{\frac{5}{2}}$

Divide.

a^{-2}	**17.** $a^5 \div a^7$
a^3	**18.** $a^2 \div a^{-1}$
x^2	**19.** $x^{\frac{3}{2}} \div x^{-\frac{1}{2}}$

Solve for *x*.

64	**20.** $x^{\frac{1}{2}} = 8$
27	**21.** $x^{\frac{4}{3}} = 81$

Reduce to lowest terms.

$2\sqrt{3}$	**22.** $\sqrt{12}$
$20\sqrt{7}$	**23.** $4\sqrt{175}$

_____$2a^2b\sqrt{5ab}$_____   **24.** $\sqrt{20a^5b^3}$

_____$\dfrac{\sqrt{6}}{3}$_____   **25.** $\sqrt{\dfrac{2}{3}}$

_____$\dfrac{\sqrt{2ay}}{2y^2}$_____   **26.** $\sqrt{\dfrac{a}{2y^3}}$

Reduce the index as small as possible.

_____$\sqrt{5}$_____   **27.** $\sqrt[4]{25}$

_____$ax\sqrt{11a}$_____   **28.** $\sqrt[4]{121a^6x^4}$

Perform the operation indicated.

_____$11\sqrt{3}$_____   **29.** $\sqrt{12} + 3\sqrt{75} - 2\sqrt{27}$

_____$3\sqrt{5}$_____   **30.** $\sqrt{3} \cdot \sqrt{15}$

_____$11 - 2\sqrt{30}$_____   **31.** $\left(\sqrt{6} - \sqrt{5}\right) \cdot \left(\sqrt{6} - \sqrt{5}\right)$

_____$2\sqrt{5}$_____   **32.** $\dfrac{10\sqrt{60}}{5\sqrt{12}}$

_____$\sqrt{3}$_____   **33.** $\dfrac{\sqrt{72}}{2\sqrt{6}}$

_____$9x\sqrt[3]{x^2}$_____   **34.** Find the square of $3\sqrt[6]{x^5}$.

_____$8ax^7\sqrt{ax}$_____   **35.** Find the cube of $2\sqrt{ax^5}$.

QUIZ 54

Algebra 1

Sections 14.1–14.2
(–8 each)

Tell if the equations are *linear* or *quadratic*.

_____quadratic_____	**1.** $x^2 + 5 = 6x$
_____linear_____	**2.** $3 + y = 7$
_____linear_____	**3.** $x + y = 6$

Give the number of real roots of a quadratic equation if the minimum point is as follows.

_____2_____	**4.** below the x-axis
_____1_____	**5.** on the x-axis
_____0_____	**6.** above the x-axis

Answer the questions about $3x^2 - 6x - 8 = 0$.

_____3_____	**7.** What is the value of a?
_____–6_____	**8.** What is the value of b?
_____–8_____	**9.** What is the value of c?

Find the minimum point of each.

_____(2,–1)_____	**10.** $y = x^2 - 4x + 3$
_____(2,–2)_____	**11.** $y = 2x^2 - 8x + 6$

QUIZ 55   *Algebra 1*

Sections 14.3–14.4
(–8 each)

Solve by finding the square root.

_____ ± 6 _____   **1.** $x^2 = 36$

_____ ± 10 _____   **2.** $x^2 = 100$

_____ ± 8 _____   **3.** $x^2 = 64$

_____ $\pm 2\sqrt{3}$ _____   **4.** $x^2 = 12$

_____ $\pm\sqrt{15}$ _____   **5.** $x^2 = 15$

_____ $\pm 3\sqrt{2}$ _____   **6.** $x^2 = 18$

_____ $\pm 2\sqrt{14}$ _____   **7.** $x^2 = 56$

_____ $\pm 2\sqrt{7}$ _____   **8.** $x^2 = 28$

_____ $\pm 2\sqrt{5}$ _____   **9.** $5x^2 = 100$

_____ $\pm\sqrt{2}$ _____   **10.** $3x^2 = 6$

Solve the word problem.

_____ length = 30 yards
width = 20 yards _____   **11.** The width of a strip of land is $\frac{2}{3}$ of its length. The area of the land is 600 square yards. What are the dimensions of the land?

$$x = \text{length}$$
$$\frac{2}{3}x = \text{width}$$
$$\frac{2}{3}x^2 = 600$$
$$\frac{3}{2} \cdot \frac{2}{3}x^2 = 600 \cdot \frac{3}{2}$$
$$x^2 = 900$$
$$\sqrt{x^2} = \sqrt{900}$$
$$x = 30 \text{ yards}$$
$$\frac{2}{3}x = 20 \text{ yards}$$

QUIZ 56   *Algebra 1*

Sections 14.6–14.7
(–8 each)

Complete the squares.

_____25_____   **1.** $x^2 + 10x + \underline{\;?\;}$

_____225_____   **2.** $x^2 - 30x + \underline{\;?\;}$

_____$\frac{9}{4}$_____   **3.** $x^2 - 3x + \underline{\;?\;}$

_____$\frac{81}{4}$_____   **4.** $x^2 + 9x + \underline{\;?\;}$

Solve by completing the squares.

_____$x = 7$_____   **5.** $x^2 - 6x = 7$

_____$x = -1$_____   **6.**

_____$x = 1$_____   **7.** $x^2 + 10x = 11$

_____$x = -11$_____   **8.**

_____$x = \dfrac{5 + \sqrt{17}}{2}$_____   **9.** $x^2 - 5x + 2 = 0$

_____$x = \dfrac{5 - \sqrt{17}}{2}$_____   **10.**

QUIZ 57 *Algebra 1*

Identify the values of *a, b,* and *c* for each quadratic equation.

$a = 1 \quad b = -2 \quad c = 7$ **1.** $x^2 - 2x + 7 = 0$

$a = 1 \quad b = 6 \quad c = -8$ **2.** $x^2 + 6x = 8$

$a = 5 \quad b = -4 \quad c = -7$ **3.** $5x^2 = 4x + 7$

$a = 4 \quad b = -8 \quad c = -3$ **4.** $4x^2 - 3 = 8x$

$a = 1 \quad b = -5 \quad c = 2$ **5.** $x^2 + 2 = 5x$

Follow the directions.

$x = \dfrac{-b \pm \sqrt{b^2 - 4ac}}{2a}$ **6.** Write the quadratic formula.

$2x^2 - 3x + 7 = 0$ **7.** Write $7 - 3x = -2x^2$ in the correct quadratic form.

Solve by using the quadratic formula.

$x = 5$ **8.** $x^2 - 6x = -5$

$x = 1$ **9.**

$x = \dfrac{1 + \sqrt{17}}{2}$ **10.** $x^2 - x = 4$

$x = \dfrac{1 - \sqrt{17}}{2}$ **11.**

TEST 12 (Final Exam)   *Algebra 1*

Units 1–14
(–2 each)

DIRECTIONS: Show all of your work neatly in pencil in the space provided. Copy your answers from your work space into the space provided for the answer. Use another sheet to keep all work and answers covered at all times.

TRUE-FALSE: If the statement is always true, write *true* in the space; if the statement is *not* always true, write *false* in the space.

_____true_____	**1.** x^{-4} may be written $\frac{1}{x^4}$.
_____false_____	**2.** The square root of x^{16} is x^4.
_____false_____	**3.** The value of $(x^2y^4z)^0$ is 0.
_____true_____	**4.** $\sqrt{27}$ can be reduced.
_____true_____	**5.** $a^4 \cdot a^{-3} = a$
_____false_____	**6.** $a^5 \div a^8 = a^3$
_____true_____	**7.** $3\sqrt{2} \cdot 4\sqrt{3} = 12\sqrt{6}$
_____false_____	**8.** $(a + b)^2 = a^2 + b^2$
_____false_____	**9.** $\sqrt{16x^4y^2} = 8x^2y$
_____true_____	**10.** $(a^2)^3 = a^6$
_____false_____	**11.** $x^{\frac{5}{3}} = \sqrt[5]{x^3}$
_____true_____	**12.** The reciprocal of $\frac{rs}{x}$ is $\frac{x}{rs}$.
_____false_____	**13.** The reciprocal of a is $\frac{a}{1}$.
_____true_____	**14.** The coordinates $(7, -4)$ are located in quadrant IV.
_____false_____	**15.** The coordinates $(8, 0)$ are located in quadrant I.
_____false_____	**16.** $3x^{-1} = \frac{1}{3x}$
_____true_____	**17.** $\frac{ax}{by} = ab^{-1}xy^{-1}$
_____true_____	**18.** $\frac{1}{5^{-2}} = 25$
_____false_____	**19.** $\sqrt{\frac{3}{5}}$ can be reduced to $\frac{\sqrt{6}}{5}$.
_____false_____	**20.** If $x^{\frac{1}{3}} = 3$, then $x = 9$.

(cont.)

MULTIPLE CHOICE: Solve the quadratic equations for the values of *x.* Write the letter of the correct choice in the space. Show your work on all multiple choice questions.

   b   **21.** $x^2 + x = 12$

     a. 6, –2   **b.** –4, 3   **c.** –3, –4   **d.** –2, 6

   d   **22.** $x^2 + x - 6 = 0$

     a. 4, –1   **b.** 3, –2   **c.** –6, 1   **d.** 2, –3

   c   **23.** $2x^2 - x - 3 = 0$

     a. 3, –1   **b.** –1, 3   **c.** $-1, \frac{3}{2}$ **d.** $\frac{1}{2}, 3$

   a   **24.** $x^2 - 5x + 2 = 0$

     a. $\frac{5 \pm \sqrt{17}}{2}$ **b.** $\frac{9}{2}, \frac{1}{2}$ **c.** $\frac{-1}{2}, \frac{-9}{2}$ **d.** 3, 2

Complete the square. (Do not solve for *x*.)

   b   **25.** $x^2 + 10x +$ __?__ .

     a. 100   **b.** 25   **c.** $\frac{25}{2}$ **d.** $\frac{25}{4}$

   d   **26.** $x^2 - 3x +$ __?__ .

     a. 9   **b.** $\frac{3}{2}$ **c.** 18   **d.** $\frac{9}{4}$

Follow the directions.

___c___ **27.** Multiply: $(7 + \sqrt{3})(7 - \sqrt{3})$

        a. $49 - \sqrt{3}$ **b.** 10 **c.** 46 **d.** 4

___a___ **28.** Add: $6\sqrt{2} + 5\sqrt{2} + \sqrt{2}$

        a. $12\sqrt{2}$ **b.** $11\sqrt{2}$ **c.** $11\sqrt{8}$ **d.** $11\sqrt{6}$

___d___ **29.** Add: $\sqrt{8} + \sqrt{98} - \sqrt{72}$

        a. $15\sqrt{2}$ **b.** 13 **c.** $84\sqrt{2}$ **d.** $3\sqrt{2}$

___d___ **30.** Multiply: $(\sqrt{7} - \sqrt{2})(\sqrt{7} - \sqrt{2})$

        a. 5 **b.** 53 **c.** $7 - 14\sqrt{2}$ **d.** $9 - 2\sqrt{14}$

___d___ **31.** Solve: $\begin{cases} 2x + 3y = 7 \\ x + y = 3 \end{cases}$

        a. $x = 2$ **b.** $x = 4$ **c.** $x = 5$ **d.** $x = 2$
          $y = -1$ $y = 1$ $y = 2$ $y = 1$

___b___ **32.** Solve: $\begin{cases} 3x - 4y = 26 \\ x - 8y = 22 \end{cases}$

        a. $x = 4$ **b.** $x = 6$ **c.** $x = 1$ **d.** $x = -3$
          $y = 3$ $y = -2$ $y = 6$ $y = 4$

(cont.)

<u> d </u> **33.** Reduce: $\sqrt{40x^3}$

       a. $2\sqrt{10x^3}$ **b.** $x\sqrt{40x}$ **c.** $10x\sqrt{2x}$ **d.** $2x\sqrt{10x}$

<u> a </u> **34.** Reduce: $\sqrt{36x^3y^2}$

       a. $6xy\sqrt{x}$ **b.** $6\sqrt{x^3y^2}$ **c.** $36\sqrt{x^3y}$ **d.** $36x^2y\sqrt{x}$

<u> d </u> **35.** Reduce: $\sqrt{\dfrac{7}{3}}$

       a. $\dfrac{\sqrt{14}}{3}$ **b.** $\sqrt{\dfrac{21}{9}}$ **c.** $\dfrac{7}{3}$ **d.** $\dfrac{\sqrt{21}}{3}$

<u> c </u> **36.** Multiply: $\dfrac{x^2-1}{6} \cdot \dfrac{2}{x-1}$

       a. $\dfrac{x^2-1}{3(x+1)}$ **b.** $\dfrac{2x^2-2}{6x+6}$ **c.** $\dfrac{x+1}{3}$ **d.** $x+1$

<u> d </u> **37.** Divide: $\dfrac{x^2-10x+21}{x^2-49} \div \dfrac{x-3}{5}$

       a. $\dfrac{5(x-7)}{x+7}$ **b.** 5 **c.** $\dfrac{5}{x-7}$ **d.** $\dfrac{5}{x+7}$

<u> b </u> **38.** Evaluate b^2-4ac when $a=1$, $b=-3$, and $c=2$.

       a. 17   **b.** 1   **c.** 11   **d.** −17

  b   **39.** Simplify: $(3x^2 + 4xy - 5y^2) + (6x^2 - 8xy + 6y^2) - (2x^2 + 6xy + 9y^2)$

          a. $7x^2 - 4xy + y^2$

          b. $7x^2 - 10xy - 8y^2$

          c. $11x^2 + 18xy - 10y^2$

          d. $7x^2 - 6xy + 2y^2$

  b   **40.** Factor: $9x^2 - 16y^2$

          a. $(3x + y)(3x - y)$

          b. $(3x + 4y)(3x - 4y)$

          c. $(9x + 16y)(9x - 16y)$

          d. $(3x - 4y)^2$

  d   **41.** Factor: $3x^2 - 2x - 8$

          a. $(3x - 4)(x + 2)$

          b. $(3x - 2)(x + 4)$

          c. $(3x + 1)(x - 8)$

          d. $(3x + 4)(x - 2)$

  d   **42.** Factor: $3x^2 - 21x + 36$

          a. $(3x - 9)(x - 4)$

          b. $(3x - 12)(x - 3)$

          c. $(3x - 18)(x - 2)$

          d. $3(x - 3)(x - 4)$

(cont.)

___c___   **43.** Expand: $(a + b - c)^2$

         a. $a^2 + b^2 - c^2 + ab - ac - bc$

         b. $a^2 + b^2 - c^2 + 2ab - 2ac - 2bc$

         c. $a^2 + b^2 + c^2 + 2ab - 2ac - 2bc$

         d. $a^2 + b^2 + c^2$

___d___   **44.** Divide: $\dfrac{2\sqrt{48}}{6\sqrt{8}}$

         a. $4\sqrt{6}$ **b.** $3\sqrt{6}$ **c.** $3\sqrt{40}$ **d.** $\dfrac{\sqrt{6}}{3}$

___b___   **45.** Add: $\dfrac{5y - 1}{2y} + \dfrac{5y + 2}{3y}$

         a. $\dfrac{5y - 7}{6y}$ **b.** $\dfrac{25y + 1}{6y}$ **c.** $25y + 1$ **d.** $\dfrac{2y - 8}{6y}$

___c___   **46.** Solve: The sum of two numbers is 71, and their difference is 13.

         a. 49, 22   **b.** 30, 41   **c.** 29, 42   **d.** 21, 50

___d___   **47.** Find the coordinates for the equation's minimum point: $y = x^2 - 4x + 3$

         a. 4,3   **b.** –2,15   **c.** –2,3   **d.** 2,–1

Quiz Solution Key

Quiz Solutions

Quiz 1

1. $6x + 2x - x = 7x$
$\quad\quad 7\left(5\right) = 35$

2. $\dfrac{3x}{4}$

$\quad \dfrac{3\left(8\right)}{4} = \dfrac{24}{4} = 6$

Quiz 2

1. $8x - \frac{1}{4} = 7\frac{3}{4}$
$\quad\quad 8x = 8$
$\quad\quad\quad x = 1$

2. $3x + 7 - 2 = 8$
$\quad\quad 3x + 5 = 8$
$\quad\quad\quad 3x = 3$
$\quad\quad\quad\quad x = 1$

3. $5x - 11 = 19$
$\quad\quad 5x = 30$
$\quad\quad\quad x = 6$

4. $\frac{5}{6}x = 25$
$\quad\quad 5x = 150$
$\quad\quad\quad x = 30$

Quiz 4

8. $\left(2a\right)^2$
$\quad \left(2 \cdot 5\right)^2$
$\quad = 10^2$
$\quad = 100$

9. $2a - 3b$
$\quad 2\left(5\right) - 3\left(3\right)$
$\quad = 10 - 9$
$\quad = 1$

10. $2a^2$
$\quad 2\left(5\right)^2$
$\quad = 2\left(25\right)$
$\quad = 50$

Quiz 5

1. $5 \cdot \left(10 - 7\right)$
$\quad = 5 \cdot 3$
$\quad = 15$

2. $\dfrac{\left(6 + 2 \cdot 8 - 4\right)}{2}$
$\quad = \dfrac{6 + 16 - 4}{2}$
$\quad = \dfrac{18}{2}$
$\quad = 9$

3. $6 + 2 \cdot \left(8 - \frac{4}{2}\right)$
$\quad = 6 + 2 \cdot \left(8 - 2\right)$
$\quad = 6 + 2 \cdot \left(6\right)$
$\quad = 6 + 12$
$\quad = 18$

5. $\left(3y\right)^2$
$\quad = \left(3 \cdot 3\right)^2$
$\quad = 9^2$
$\quad = 81$

6. $3y^2$
$\quad = 3 \cdot \left(3^2\right)$
$\quad = 3\left(9\right)$
$\quad = 27$

Quiz 7

1. let x = amount earned for one hour

   $2x = \$10.80$

   $x = \$5.40$

   $5(\$5.40) = \$27.00$

2. $4(\$5.40) = \$21.60$

3. $i = \$500(.06)(4)$

   $i = \$120$

6. $A = 3.14(4^2)$

   $A = 3.14(16)$

   $A = 50.24$ yd.^{2}

Quiz 8

1. $F = \frac{9}{5}(60°) + 32°$

   $F = 108° + 32°$

   $F = 140°$

2. $C = \frac{5}{9}(50° - 32°)$

   $C = \frac{5}{9}(18°)$

   $C = 10°$

Quiz 10

7. $-3 + (-14) = -3 - 14 = -17$

8. $-12 + 8 + (-6) + 2 + 2 = -12 + 8 - 6 + 2 + 2 = -6$

9. $20 - (-6) = 20 + 6 = 26$

Quiz 11

7. $-6^2 = -1(6^2) = -1(36) = -36$

8. $(-5)^3 = (-5)(-5)(-5) = -125$

9. $(-8)^2 = (-8)(-8) = 64$

Quiz 12

6. $14m^2 - (-11m^2) = 14m^2 + 11m^2 = 25m^2$

7. $3(y - 2) - [-3(y - 2)] = 3(y - 2) + 3(y - 2) = 6(y - 2)$

8. $-7x^2y - (-8x^2y) = -7x^2y + 8x^2y = x^2y$

Quiz 13

1. $6x^2 - 2xy + 3y^2 - \left(4x^2 - 3xy - 2y^2\right)$

    $= 6x^2 - 2xy + 3y^2 - 4x^2 + 3xy + 2y^2$

    $= 2x^2 + xy + 5y^2$

2. $6x^2 - 2xy + 3y^2 - \left(-x^2 - xy - y^2\right)$

    $= 6x^2 - 2xy + 3y^2 + x^2 + xy + y^2$

    $= 7x^2 - xy + 4y^2$

3. $6x^2 - 2xy + 3y^2 - \left(-2x^2 + 4xy - 7y^2\right)$

    $= 6x^2 - 2xy + 3y^2 + 2x^2 - 4xy + 7y^2$

    $= 8x^2 - 6xy + 10y^2$

4. $a^2 - b^2 + ab + a^2 + b^2$

    $= 2a^2 + ab$

5. $ab - \left(a^2 - b^2\right) - \left(a^2 + b^2\right)$

    $= ab - a^2 + b^2 - a^2 - b^2$

    $= ab - 2a^2$

7. $\dfrac{2x + 4}{3} = 13 + 7$

    $\dfrac{2x + 4}{3} = 20$

    $2x + 4 = 60$

    $2x = 56$

    $x = 28$

8. $4x + 5 = 3x - 8$

    $x + 5 = -8$

    $x = -13$

9. $6x - 10 = 4\left(x + 3\right)$

    $6x - 10 = 4x + 12$

    $2x = 22$

    $x = 11$

Quiz 14

8. $3x - \left(2x - 7y\right)$

    $= 3x - 2x + 7y$

    $= x + 7y$

9. $4x^2 - 2xy + y^2 - \left(2xy + 3x^2 - 3y^2\right) + \left(x^2 - xy - y^2\right)$

    $= 4x^2 - 2xy + y^2 - 2xy - 3x^2 + 3y^2 + x^2 - xy + y^2$

    $= 2x^2 - 5xy + 3y^2$

10. $xy - \left[xy + xz - x - \left(2x - xz\right) + 2x - 2xz\right] - x$

    $= xy - \left(xy + xz - x - 2x + xz + 2x - 2xz\right) - x$

    $= xy - xy - xz + x + 2x - xz - 2x + 2xz - x$

    $= 0$

Quiz 15

2. $-3ab + 4ac - 2ad = -\left(3ab - 4ac + 2ad\right)$

4. $a^3 - a^2 + a - 1 = \left(a^3 - a^2\right) - \left(-a + 1\right)$

3. $a^2 + ab - 2b^2 = -\left(-a^2 - ab + 2b^2\right)$

Quiz 16

8. $(x + 3)(x - 2)$

$= x^2 - 2x + 3x - 6$

$= x^2 + x - 6$

9. $(2b + 1)(3b - 5)$

$= 6b^2 - 10b + 3b - 5$

$= 6b^2 - 7b - 5$

Quiz 18

8. $\dfrac{15a^4 b - 10ab^3}{-5ab} = \dfrac{-5ab\left(-3a^3 + 2b^2\right)}{-5ab} = -3a^3 + 2b^2$

10. $\dfrac{24x^5 y^2 z - 16x^7 y^3 z^2 + 3bx^{10} y^2 z^2}{4xy^2 z} = \dfrac{4xy^2 z\left(6x^4 - 4x^6 yz + 9x^9 z\right)}{4xy^2 z} = 6x^4 - 4x^6 yz + 9x^9 z$

Quiz 21

1. $7^0 = 1$

2. $x^3 \cdot x^4 = x^7$

4. $6a - (-3a) = 9a$

5. $(x + 4)(x - 3)$

$= x^2 - 3x + 4x - 12$

$= x^2 + x - 12$

6. $(2x + 5)(3x - 4)$

$= 6x^2 - 8x + 15x - 20$

$= 6x^2 + 7x - 20$

7. $(x^2 + y)(x^2 - y)$

$= x^4 - x^2 y + x^2 y - y^2$

$= x^4 - y^2$

8. $(.2x + .3y)(.2x + .1y)$

$= .04x^2 + .02xy + .06xy + .03y^2$

$= .04x^2 + .08xy + .03y^2$

9. $(x^2 y^4 + bc)(x^2 y^4 + bc)$

$= x^4 y^8 + bcx^2 y^4 + bcx^2 y^4 + b^2 c^2$

$= x^4 y^8 + 2bcx^2 y^4 + b^2 c^2$

Quiz 22

7. $(3x - 2y)^2$

$= (3x - 2y)(3x - 2y)$

$= 9x^2 - 6xy - 6xy + 4y^2$

$= 9x^2 - 12xy + 4y^2$

8. $\left(x - \frac{1}{2}\right)^2$

$= \left(x - \frac{1}{2}\right)\left(x - \frac{1}{2}\right)$

$= x^2 - \frac{1}{2}x - \frac{1}{2}x + \frac{1}{4}$

$= x^2 - x + \frac{1}{4}$

9. $(4x^2 + 3b^2)(4x^2 - 3b^2)$

$= 16x^4 - 12x^2 b^2 + 12x^2 b^2 - 9b^4$

$= 16x^4 - 9b^4$

10. $\left(\frac{1}{2}a + 2\right)\left(\frac{1}{2}a - 2\right)$

$= \frac{1}{4}a^2 - a + a - 4$

$= \frac{1}{4}a^2 - 4$

Quiz 24

7. $3x^5 - 3x$

$= 3x\left(x^4 - 1\right)$

$= 3x\left(x^2 + 1\right)\left(x^2 - 1\right)$

$= 3x\left(x^2 + 1\right)\left(x + 1\right)\left(x - 1\right)$

9. $4x^2 + 28x + 48$

$= 4\left(x^2 + 7x + 12\right)$

$= 4\left(x + 4\right)\left(x + 3\right)$

10. $2x^2 - 12x + 10$

$= 2\left(x^2 - 6x + 5\right)$

$= 2\left(x - 5\right)\left(x - 1\right)$

Quiz 26

9. $a^2 - \left(b + c\right)^2$

$= \left[a + \left(b + c\right)\right]\left[a - \left(b + c\right)\right]$

$= \left(a + b + c\right)\left(a - b - c\right)$

10. $4c^2 - \left(b + c\right)^2$

$= \left[2c + \left(b + c\right)\right]\left[2c - \left(b + c\right)\right]$

$= \left(2c + b + c\right)\left(2c - b - c\right)$

$= \left(3c + b\right)\left(c - b\right)$

Quiz 27

4. $m^4 - 1$

$= \left(m^2 + 1\right)\left(m^2 - 1\right)$

$= \left(m^2 + 1\right)\left(m + 1\right)\left(m - 1\right)$

Quiz 28

6. $x^2 - 6x + 9 = 0$

$\left(x - 3\right)\left(x - 3\right) = 0$

$x = 3 \quad x = 3$

7. $9x^2 = 64$

$x^2 = \frac{64}{9}$

$x = \sqrt{\frac{64}{9}}$

$x = \pm\frac{8}{3} \ \text{ or } \pm 2\frac{2}{3}$

8. $7x^2 - 28 = 0$

$7x^2 = 28$

$x^2 = 4$

$x = \sqrt{4}$

$x = \pm 2$

9. $2x^2 - 12 = 5x$

$2x^2 - 5x - 12 = 0$

$\left(2x + 3\right)\left(x - 4\right) = 0$

$x = -\frac{3}{2} \quad x = 4$

Quiz 29

4. $-\dfrac{-x}{-a - b} = -\dfrac{-x}{-\left(a + b\right)} = -\dfrac{x}{a + b}$

8. $\dfrac{1}{2} - \dfrac{3}{8} + \dfrac{3}{4} = \dfrac{4}{8} - \dfrac{3}{8} + \dfrac{6}{8} = \dfrac{7}{8}$

7. $\dfrac{\frac{2}{3}}{\frac{8}{9}} = \dfrac{2}{3} \cdot \dfrac{9}{8} = \dfrac{3}{4}$

9. $5\frac{1}{4} \cdot 2\frac{2}{7} = \dfrac{21}{4} \cdot \dfrac{16}{7} = 12$

Quiz 30

7. $\dfrac{2x}{4x^2 - 6ax} = \dfrac{2x}{2x(2x - 3a)} = \dfrac{1}{2x - 3a}$

8. $\dfrac{5a + 10b}{5c + 15d} = \dfrac{5(a + 2b)}{5(c + 3d)} = \dfrac{a + 2b}{c + 3d}$

9. $\dfrac{(a + b)^2}{a^2 - b^2} = \dfrac{(a + b)(a + b)}{(a + b)(a - b)} = \dfrac{a + b}{a - b}$

10. $\dfrac{3b^3}{3b + 3} = \dfrac{3b^3}{3(b + 1)} = \dfrac{b^3}{b + 1}$

Quiz 31

1. $\dfrac{x}{2y} = \dfrac{x(2a)}{2y(2a)} = \dfrac{2ax}{4ay}$

2. $\dfrac{1}{x + 2} = \dfrac{1(x - 2)}{(x + 2)(x - 2)} = \dfrac{x - 2}{x^2 - 4}$

3. $\dfrac{y^2}{y + 1} = \dfrac{y^2(y + 1)}{(y + 1)(y + 1)} = \dfrac{y^2(y + 1)}{y^2 + 2y + 1}$ or $\dfrac{y^3 + y^2}{y^2 + 2y + 1}$

7. $\dfrac{a}{x^2 - y^2} , \dfrac{b}{x + y} = \dfrac{a}{(x + y)(x - y)} , \dfrac{b}{x + y}$

   $\text{LCD} = (x + y)(x - y)$

8. $\dfrac{12}{x^2 - 3x} , \dfrac{5}{x^2 - 5x + 6} = \dfrac{12}{x(x - 3)} , \dfrac{5}{(x - 3)(x - 2)}$

   $\text{LCD} = x(x - 3)(x + 2)$

10. $\dfrac{ax + b}{x} = \dfrac{ax}{x} + \dfrac{b}{x} = a + \dfrac{b}{x}$

Quiz 32

4. $\dfrac{4}{7a} = \dfrac{4(2ab)}{7a(2ab)} = \dfrac{8ab}{14a^2b}$

5. $\dfrac{1}{a+b} = \dfrac{1(a+b)}{(a+b)(a+b)} = \dfrac{a+b}{a^2+2ab+b^2}$

6. $\dfrac{2}{a-b} = \dfrac{2(a+b)}{(a-b)(a+b)} = \dfrac{2(a+b)}{a^2-b^2}$

7. $\dfrac{2a}{3} + \dfrac{3a}{4} = \dfrac{2a(4)}{3(4)} + \dfrac{3a(3)}{4(3)} = \dfrac{8a}{12} + \dfrac{9a}{12} = \dfrac{17a}{12}$

8. $\dfrac{3x+4}{2x} + \dfrac{x-6}{3x}$

$= \dfrac{(3x+4)(3)}{2x(3)} + \dfrac{(x-6)(2)}{3x(2)}$

$= \dfrac{9x+12+2x-12}{6x} = \dfrac{11x}{6x} = \dfrac{11}{6}$ or $1\frac{5}{6}$

9. $\dfrac{x+2}{12} - \dfrac{x-3}{3} + \dfrac{3x}{4}$

$= \dfrac{x+2}{12} - \dfrac{(x-3)(4)}{3(4)} + \dfrac{(3x)(3)}{4(3)}$

$= \dfrac{x+2}{12} - \dfrac{4x-12}{12} + \dfrac{9x}{12}$

$= \dfrac{x+2-4x+12+9x}{12}$

$= \dfrac{6x+14}{12} = \dfrac{2(3x+7)}{12} = \dfrac{3x+7}{6}$

Quiz 33

6. $\dfrac{x^2+3x+2}{x^2-3x-10} \cdot \dfrac{x^2-6x+5}{x^2+8x+7} = \dfrac{(x+2)(x+1)}{(x+2)(x-5)} \cdot \dfrac{(x-1)(x-5)}{(x+7)(x+1)} = \dfrac{x-1}{x+7}$

7. $\dfrac{5mn}{6bx} \div \dfrac{10m^2n}{3ax^2} = \dfrac{5mn}{6bx} \cdot \dfrac{3ax^2}{10m^2n} = \dfrac{ax}{4bm}$

8. $\dfrac{3abm}{7} \div abx = \dfrac{3abm}{7} \cdot \dfrac{1}{abx} = \dfrac{3m}{7x}$

9. $(4a+2) \div \dfrac{2a+1}{5a} = (4a+2) \cdot \dfrac{5a}{2a+1} = \dfrac{2(2a+1)}{1} \cdot \dfrac{5a}{2a+1} = 10a$

10. $\dfrac{\frac{2b}{3c}}{\frac{4b^2}{9c^2}} = \dfrac{2b}{3c} \div \dfrac{4b^2}{9c^2} = \dfrac{2b}{3c} \cdot \dfrac{9c^2}{4b^2} = \dfrac{3c}{2b}$

Quiz 34

1. $\dfrac{x^2}{y} \div \dfrac{2x^2}{y^2} = \dfrac{x^2}{y} \cdot \dfrac{y^2}{2x^2} = \dfrac{y}{2}$

2. $\dfrac{6c}{5b} \div \dfrac{18c^2}{7b^3} = \dfrac{6c}{5b} \cdot \dfrac{7b^3}{18c^2} = \dfrac{7b^2}{15c}$

4. $\dfrac{\frac{x^2}{y^2}}{\frac{x}{y}} = \dfrac{x^2}{y^2} \div \dfrac{x}{y} = \dfrac{x^2}{y^2} \cdot \dfrac{y}{x} = \dfrac{x}{y}$

5. $\dfrac{x}{2} + \dfrac{x}{6} = \dfrac{10}{3}$

$\dfrac{x(3)}{2(3)} + \dfrac{x}{6} = \dfrac{10(2)}{3(2)}$

$\dfrac{3x}{6} + \dfrac{x}{6} = \dfrac{20}{6}$

$\dfrac{4x}{6} = \dfrac{20}{6}$

$4x = 20$

$x = 5$

6. $2x + \dfrac{x}{3} = \dfrac{35}{3}$

$\dfrac{2x(3)}{3} + \dfrac{x}{3} = \dfrac{35}{3}$

$\dfrac{6x}{3} + \dfrac{x}{3} = \dfrac{35}{3}$

$\dfrac{7x}{3} = \dfrac{35}{3}$

$7x = 35$

$x = 5$

7. $\dfrac{3x}{4} + \dfrac{7x}{16} - \dfrac{x}{2} - \dfrac{9x}{16} = \dfrac{1}{8}$

$\dfrac{3x(4)}{4(4)} + \dfrac{7x}{16} - \dfrac{x(8)}{2(8)} - \dfrac{9x}{16} = \dfrac{1(2)}{8(2)}$

$\dfrac{12x}{16} + \dfrac{7x}{16} - \dfrac{8x}{16} - \dfrac{9x}{16} = \dfrac{2}{16}$

$\dfrac{2x}{16} = \dfrac{2}{16}$

$2x = 2$

$x = 1$

Quiz 35

1. $\dfrac{12x}{5y} \cdot \dfrac{15y^2}{36x^2} = \dfrac{12x}{5y} \cdot \dfrac{15y^2}{36x^2} = \dfrac{y}{x}$

2. $\dfrac{3r^2}{9r^3} \div \dfrac{8r^4}{6r^5} = \dfrac{3r^2}{9r^3} \cdot \dfrac{6r^5}{8r^4} = \dfrac{1}{4}$

3. $\dfrac{y}{3} + \dfrac{y}{2} = 40$

$\dfrac{y(2)}{3(2)} + \dfrac{y(3)}{2(3)} = \dfrac{40(6)}{6}$

$\dfrac{2y}{6} + \dfrac{3y}{6} = \dfrac{240}{6}$

$\dfrac{5y}{6} = \dfrac{240}{6}$

$5y = 240$

$y = 48$

4. $\dfrac{5c}{8} - \dfrac{c}{3} = \dfrac{5c}{6} - 13$

$\dfrac{5c(3)}{8(3)} - \dfrac{c(8)}{3(8)} = \dfrac{5c(4)}{6(4)} - \dfrac{13(24)}{24}$

$\dfrac{15c}{24} - \dfrac{8c}{24} = \dfrac{20c}{24} - \dfrac{312}{24}$

$\dfrac{7c}{24} = \dfrac{20c - 312}{24}$

$7c = 20c - 312$

$-13c = -312$

$c = 24$

Quiz 35 continued

5. $\dfrac{3}{a} = \dfrac{19}{3a} - \dfrac{5}{3}$

$\dfrac{3(3)}{a(3)} = \dfrac{19}{3a} - \dfrac{5(a)}{3(a)}$

$\dfrac{9}{3a} = \dfrac{19}{3a} - \dfrac{5a}{3a}$

$9 = 19 - 5a$

$5a = 10$

$a = 2$

6. $\dfrac{2}{m} = \dfrac{5}{3m - 1}$

$\dfrac{2(3m - 1)}{m(3m - 1)} = \dfrac{5(m)}{(3m - 1)(m)}$

$\dfrac{6m - 2}{3m^2 - m} = \dfrac{5m}{3m^2 - m}$

$6m - 2 = 5m$

$m = 2$

Quiz 36

1. $\dfrac{\$14}{\$7} = \dfrac{2}{1}$

2. $\dfrac{5 \text{ inches}}{1 \text{ yard}} = \dfrac{5 \text{ inches}}{36 \text{ inches}} = \dfrac{5}{36}$

3. $\dfrac{3 \text{ days}}{1 \text{ week}} = \dfrac{3 \text{ days}}{7 \text{ days}} = \dfrac{3}{7}$

4. $\dfrac{25\cent}{\$1.00} = \dfrac{25\cent}{100\cent} = \dfrac{25}{100} = \dfrac{1}{4}$

5. $\dfrac{10 \text{ days}}{12 \text{ days}} = \dfrac{10}{12} = \dfrac{5}{6}$

6. $\dfrac{2 \text{ quarts}}{1 \text{ gallon}} = \dfrac{2 \text{ quarts}}{4 \text{ quarts}} = \dfrac{2}{4} = \dfrac{1}{2}$

7. $4:16 = \dfrac{4}{16} = \dfrac{1}{4}$

8. $19:38 = \dfrac{19}{38} = \dfrac{1}{2}$

9. $5.2:1 = \dfrac{5.2}{1} = \dfrac{52}{10} = \dfrac{26}{5}$

10. $3:6 = \dfrac{3}{6} = \dfrac{1}{2}$

11. $210:30 = \dfrac{210}{30} = \dfrac{7}{1}$

12. $\dfrac{1}{8}$ to $3 = \dfrac{\frac{1}{8}}{3} = \dfrac{1}{8} \div \dfrac{3}{1} = \dfrac{1}{8} \cdot \dfrac{1}{3} = \dfrac{1}{24}$

13. 4 to $.7 = \dfrac{4}{.7} = \dfrac{40}{7}$

14. $\dfrac{1.6}{2.6} = \dfrac{16}{26} = \dfrac{8}{13}$

15. $2\dfrac{1}{4}$ to $5 = \dfrac{2\frac{1}{4}}{5} = \dfrac{\frac{9}{4}}{5} = \dfrac{9}{4} \div 5 = \dfrac{9}{4} \cdot \dfrac{1}{5} = \dfrac{9}{20}$

Quiz 37

4. $\frac{2}{3} = \frac{4}{x}$

$2x = 4(3)$

$2x = 12$

$x = 6$

5. $\frac{5}{x} = \frac{4}{3}$

$5(3) = 4x$

$15 = 4x$

$x = \frac{15}{4}$ or $3\frac{3}{4}$

6. $\frac{x + 2}{x} = \frac{10}{6}$

$(x + 2)(6) = 10x$

$6x + 12 = 10x$

$12 = 4x$

$x = 3$

7. $\frac{x}{x - 1} = \frac{15}{12}$

$12x = 15(x - 1)$

$12x = 15x - 15$

$15 = 3x$

$x = 5$

8. $\frac{a^2 - b^2}{(a - b)^2} = \frac{(a + b)(a - b)}{(a - b)(a - b)} = \frac{a + b}{a - b}$

9. $\frac{\frac{3}{4}}{\frac{1}{4}} = \frac{3}{4} \div \frac{1}{4} = \frac{3}{4} \cdot \frac{4}{1} = \frac{12}{4} = \frac{3}{1}$

Quiz 38

6. $12x$ to $6x = \frac{12x}{6x} = \frac{2}{1}$

7. $\frac{4}{5}x$ to $\frac{2}{5}x^2 = \frac{\frac{4}{5}x}{\frac{2}{5}x^2} = \frac{4}{5}x \div \frac{2}{5}x^2 = \frac{4x}{5} \cdot \frac{5}{2x^2} = \frac{2}{x}$

8. $\frac{4}{9} = \frac{4(5)}{9(5)} = \frac{20}{45}$

$\frac{2}{5} = \frac{2(9)}{5(9)} = \frac{18}{45}$

9. $\frac{105}{p'} = \frac{3}{5}$

$3p' = 525$

$p' = 175$

10. $\frac{81 \text{ sq. ft.}}{A'} = \frac{(21 \text{ ft.})^2}{(42 \text{ ft.})^2}$

$\frac{81 \text{ sq. ft.}}{A'} = \frac{441 \text{ sq. ft.}}{1764 \text{ sq. ft.}}$

$A'(441 \text{ sq. ft.}) = (1764 \text{ sq. ft.})(81 \text{ sq. ft.})$

$A' = \frac{(1764 \text{ sq. ft.})(81 \text{ sq. ft.})}{(441 \text{ sq. ft.})}$

$A' = 324 \text{ sq. ft.}$

Quiz 39

2. $\frac{3}{5}x = 3.6$

$5\left(\frac{3}{5}x\right) = 5(3.6)$

$3x = 18$

$x = 6$

3. $5x - 4 = 16$

$5x = 20$

$x = 4$

4. $\frac{3}{8}x + 7 = 13$

$\frac{3}{8}x = 6$

$3x = 48$

$x = 16$

6. $9x + 7 = 7x - 5$

$2x = -12$

$x = -6$

7. $2x - \frac{x}{6} = 11$

$\frac{2x(6)}{6} - \frac{x}{6} = \frac{11(6)}{6}$

$\frac{12x}{6} - \frac{x}{6} = \frac{66}{6}$

$12x - x = 66$

$11x = 66$

$x = 6$

8. $\frac{4}{7} = \frac{8}{x + 2}$

$4(x + 2) = 8(7)$

$4x + 8 = 56$

$4x = 48$

$x = 12$

9. $3x - (2x + 7) = 15$

$3x - 2x - 7 = 15$

$x = 22$

10. $(x + 2)^2 = (x + 2)(x - 2)$

$x^2 + 4x + 4 = x^2 - 4$

$4x + 4 = -4$

$4x = -8$

$x = -2$

Quiz 40

5. $abx = ab$

$\frac{abx}{ab} = \frac{ab}{ab}$

$x = 1$

6. $bx + c = y$

$bx = y - c$

$x = \frac{y - c}{b}$

9. $t = \frac{spc^2}{d}$

$td = spc^2$

$d = \frac{spc^2}{t}$

10. $I = \frac{E}{R + r}$

$I(R + r) = E$

$IR + Ir = E$

$Ir = E - IR$

$r = \frac{E - IR}{I}$

Quiz 43

1. $x + 5y = 20$
Let $y = 0$
$x + 5(0) = 20$
$x = 20$
$(20, 0)$

2. $3x - 2y = 27$
Let $y = 0$
$3x - 2(0) = 27$
$3x = 27$
$x = 9$
$(9, 0)$

3. $y - 2x = 8$
Let $x = 0$
$y - 2(0) = 8$
$y = 8$
$(0, 8)$

4. $21 - 3y = 7x$
Let $x = 0$
$21 - 3y = 7(0)$
$21 - 3y = 0$
$21 = 3y$
$7 = y$
$(0, 7)$

5. $\begin{cases} x + y = 4 \\ x - y = 6 \end{cases}$
$2x = 10$
$x = 5$

6. $\begin{cases} x + y = 4 \\ 5 + y = 4 \end{cases}$
$y = -1$

7. $\begin{cases} 2x - y = 9 \\ 3x + y = 6 \end{cases}$
$5x = 15$
$x = 3$

8. $3x + y = 6$
$3(3) + y = 6$
$9 + y = 6$
$y = -3$

9. $\begin{cases} y = x - 4 \\ y = -2x + 5 \end{cases}$
$x - 4 = -2x + 5$
$3x = 9$
$x = 3$

10. $y = x - 4$
$y = 3 - 4$
$y = -1$

11. $\begin{cases} x + 4y = -10 \\ 2x - y = 7 \end{cases}$
$-y = 7 - 2x$
$y = -7 + 2x$
$x + 4(-7 + 2x) = -10$
$x - 28 + 8x = -10$
$9x - 28 = -10$
$9x = 18$
$x = 2$

12. $2x - y = 7$
$2(2) - y = 7$
$4 - y = 7$
$-3 = y$

Quiz 44

7. $\begin{cases} 3x + 2y = 23 \\ x + y = 16 \end{cases}$

$\begin{cases} 3x + 2y = 23 \\ -2(x + y) = -2(16) \end{cases}$

$\begin{cases} 3x + 2y = 23 \\ -2x - 2y = -32 \end{cases}$
$x = -9$
$x + y = 16$
$-9 + y = 16$
$y = 25$
$(-9, 25)$

8. $\begin{cases} 2x + 3y = 15 \\ 3x + 2y = 0 \end{cases}$

$\begin{cases} 3(2x + 3y) = 3(15) \\ -2(3x + 2y) = -2(0) \end{cases}$

$\begin{cases} 6x + 9y = 45 \\ -6x - 4y = 0 \end{cases}$
$5y = 45$
$y = 9$
$3x + 2y = 0$
$3x + 2(9) = 0$
$3x + 18 = 0$
$3x = -18$
$x = -6$
$(-6, 9)$

Quiz 45

7–8. $\begin{cases} ax + by = r \\ ax + cy = s \end{cases}$

$$by - cy = r - s$$
$$y(b - c) = r \pm s$$
$$y = \frac{r - s}{b - c}$$

$$ax + by = r$$
$$ax + b\left(\frac{r - s}{b - c}\right) = r$$
$$ax + \frac{br - bs}{b - c} = r$$
$$ax = r - \frac{br - bs}{b - c}$$
$$ax = \frac{r(b - c)}{b - c} - \frac{br - bs}{b - c}$$
$$ax = \frac{br - cr - br + bs}{b - c}$$
$$ax = \frac{-cr + bs}{b - c}$$
$$x = \frac{-cr + bs}{a(b - c)}$$
$$x = \frac{-cr + bs}{ab - ac}$$
$$x = \frac{-(cr - bs)}{-(ac - ab)}$$
$$x = \frac{cr - bs}{ac - ab}$$

9–10. $\begin{cases} cx + ry = m \\ dx - sy = n \end{cases}$

$\begin{cases} s(cx + ry) = s(m) \\ r(dx - sy) = r(n) \end{cases}$

$\begin{cases} csx + rsy = ms \\ drx - rsy = nr \end{cases}$

$$csx + drx = ms + nr$$
$$x(cs + dr) = ms + nr$$
$$x = \frac{ms + nr}{cs + dr}$$

$$cx + ry = m$$
$$c\left(\frac{ms + nr}{cs + dr}\right) + ry = m$$
$$\frac{cms + cnr}{cs + dr} + ry = m$$
$$ry = m - \frac{cms + cnr}{cs + dr}$$
$$ry = \frac{m(cs + dr)}{cs + dr} - \frac{cms + cnr}{cs + dr}$$
$$ry = \frac{cms + dmr - cms - cnr}{cs + dr}$$
$$y = \frac{dmr - cnr}{r(cs + dr)}$$
$$y = \frac{r(dm - cn)}{r(cs + dr)}$$
$$y = \frac{dm - cn}{cs + dr}$$

177

Quiz 46

1. $\left(5x^5y^2\right)^2 = 5^2 \cdot \left(x^5\right)^2 \cdot \left(y^2\right)^2 = 25x^{10}y^4$

2. $\left(-3x^2y^5\right)^3 = \left(-3\right)^3 \cdot \left(x^2\right)^3 \cdot \left(y^5\right)^3 = -27x^6y^{15}$

3. $\left(\dfrac{-2x^2}{3y}\right)^4 = \dfrac{\left(-2\right)^4 \cdot \left(x^2\right)^4}{3^4 \cdot y^4} = \dfrac{16x^8}{81y^4}$

4. $\left(\dfrac{x^2y^2}{xy^3}\right)^n = \dfrac{\left(x^2\right)^n \cdot \left(y^2\right)^n}{x^n \cdot \left(y^3\right)^n} = \dfrac{x^{2n}y^{2n}}{x^ny^{3n}}$

5. $\left(5m^2 - 6\right)^2 = \left(5m^2 - 6\right)\left(5m^2 - 6\right)$

$$= 25m^4 - 30m^2 - 30m^2 + 36$$
$$= 25m^4 - 60m^2 + 36$$

6. $\left(a + b - c\right)^2 = \left(a + b - c\right)\left(a + b - c\right)$

$$= a^2 + ab - ac + ab + b^2 - bc - ac - bc + c^2$$
$$= a^2 + b^2 + c^2 + 2ab - 2ac - 2bc$$

7. $\left(3a + 2b - 4c\right)^2 = \left(3a + 2b - 4c\right)\left(3a + 2b - 4c\right)$

$$= 9a^2 + 6ab - 12ac + 6ab + 4b^2 - 8bc - 12ac - 8bc + 16c^2$$
$$= 9a^2 + 4b^2 + 16c^2 + 12ab - 24ac - 16bc$$

8. $\left(x + y\right)^3 = \left(x + y\right)\left(x + y\right)\left(x + y\right)$

$$= \left(x + y\right)\left(x^2 + 2xy + y^2\right)$$
$$= x^3 + 2x^2y + xy^2 + x^2y + 2xy^2 + y^3$$
$$= x^3 + 3x^2y + 3xy^2 + y^3$$

Quiz 47

1. $\left(3a^2b^3\right)^3 = 3^3 \cdot \left(a^2\right)^3 \cdot \left(b^3\right)^3 = 27a^6b^9$

2. $\left(-2x^2y^5\right)^5 = \left(-2\right)^5 \cdot \left(x^2\right)^5 \cdot \left(y^5\right)^5 = -32x^{10}y^{25}$

3. $\left(\dfrac{-2}{3a^3}\right)^2 = \dfrac{\left(-2\right)^2}{3^2 \cdot \left(a^3\right)^2} = \dfrac{4}{9a^6}$

4. $\left(\dfrac{6a^2}{5b^3}\right)^n = \dfrac{6^n \cdot \left(a^2\right)^n}{5^n \cdot \left(b^3\right)^n} = \dfrac{6^n a^{2n}}{5^n b^{3n}}$

5. $\sqrt[3]{8a^3b^{15}} = \left(8a^3b^{15}\right)^{\frac{1}{3}} = 8^{\frac{1}{3}}a^{\frac{3}{3}}b^{\frac{15}{3}} = 2^{\frac{3}{3}}ab^5 = 2ab^5$

6. $\sqrt[4]{16x^8y^{12}} = \left(2^4x^8y^{12}\right)^{\frac{1}{4}} = 2^{\frac{4}{4}}x^{\frac{8}{4}}y^{\frac{12}{4}} = 2x^2y^3$

7. $\sqrt{\dfrac{81x^6y^4}{121a^4b^2z^{10}}} = \left(\dfrac{9^2x^6y^4}{11^2a^4b^2z^{10}}\right)^{\frac{1}{2}} = \dfrac{9^{\frac{2}{2}}x^{\frac{6}{2}}y^{\frac{4}{2}}}{11^{\frac{2}{2}}a^{\frac{4}{2}}b^{\frac{2}{2}}z^{\frac{10}{2}}} = \dfrac{9x^3y^2}{11a^2bz^5}$

8. $\sqrt[6]{\dfrac{\left(a-b\right)^{12}}{64a^{12}}} = \left(\dfrac{\left(a-b\right)^{12}}{2^6a^{12}}\right)^{\frac{1}{6}} = \dfrac{\left(a-b\right)^{\frac{12}{6}}}{2^{\frac{6}{6}}a^{\frac{12}{6}}} = \dfrac{\left(a-b\right)^2}{2a^2}$

9. $\sqrt{1225} = \sqrt{5 \cdot 5 \cdot 7 \cdot 7} = 5 \cdot 7 = 35$

10. $\sqrt{441} = \sqrt{3 \cdot 3 \cdot 7 \cdot 7} = 3 \cdot 7 = 21$

Quiz 48

1.

$$x^2 + 6x + 9 \quad \underline{|x + 3}$$

$$\frac{x^2}{}$$

$$2x \quad \big| 6x + 9$$

$$2x + 3 \quad \big| 6x + 9$$

4.

$$4x^2 + 12x + 9 \quad \underline{|2x + 3}$$

$$\frac{4x^2}{}$$

$$4x \quad \big| 12x + 9$$

$$4x + 3 \quad \big| 12x + 9$$

2.

$$9x^2 - 6x + 1 \quad \underline{|3x - 1}$$

$$\frac{9x^2}{}$$

$$6x \quad \big| -6x + 1$$

$$6x - 1 \quad \big| -6x + 1$$

5.

$$\sqrt{9801}$$

$$\overline{98}\,\overline{01} \quad \underline{|99}$$

$$81$$

$$18 \quad 17\,01$$

$$189 \quad 17\,01$$

3.

$$\frac{9x^2}{y^2} + 18 + \frac{9y^2}{x^2} \quad \underline{\left| \frac{3x}{y} + \frac{3y}{x} \right.}$$

$$\frac{9x^2}{y^2}$$

$$\frac{6x}{y} \quad \bigg| 18 + \frac{9y^2}{x^2}$$

$$\frac{6x}{y} + \frac{3y}{x} \quad \bigg| 18 + \frac{9y^2}{x^2}$$

6.

$$\sqrt{\frac{361}{961}}$$

$$\sqrt{361}$$

$$\overline{03}\,\overline{61} \quad \underline{|19}$$

$$1$$

$$2 \quad 2\,61$$

$$29 \quad 2\,61$$

$$\sqrt{961}$$

$$\overline{09}\,\overline{61} \quad \underline{|31}$$

$$9$$

$$6 \quad 61$$

$$61 \quad 61$$

$$\sqrt{\frac{361}{961}} = \frac{19}{31}$$

Quiz 49

2. $2^{-2} = \dfrac{1}{2^2} = \dfrac{1}{4}$

3. $\left(-\dfrac{1}{2}\right)^{-2} = (-2)^2 = 4$

4. $a^3\left(a^{-2}\right) = a^{3-2} = a^1 = a$

5. $\left(x^{\frac{1}{2}}\right)\left(x^{\frac{1}{2}}\right) = x^{\frac{1}{2}+\frac{1}{2}} = x^1 = x$

7. $x^4 \div x^{-4} = x^4 \div \dfrac{1}{x^4} = x^4 \cdot x^4 = x^8$

10. $x^{\frac{1}{3}} = 3$

$\left(x^{\frac{1}{3}}\right)^3 = 3^3$

$x = 27$

11. $x^{\frac{1}{2}} = 5$

$\left(x^{\frac{1}{2}}\right)^2 = 5^2$

$x = 25$

Quiz 51

2. $\sqrt{18} = \sqrt{2 \cdot 3 \cdot 3} = 3\sqrt{2}$

3. $\sqrt[3]{24} = \sqrt[3]{2 \cdot 2 \cdot 2 \cdot 3} = 2\sqrt[3]{3}$

4. $\sqrt{50a^3} = \sqrt{2 \cdot 5 \cdot 5 \cdot a \cdot a \cdot a} = 5a\sqrt{2a}$

5. $\sqrt[3]{16x^2y^5z^7} = \left(2^4 \cdot x^2 \cdot y^5 \cdot z^7\right)^{\frac{1}{3}} = 2^{\frac{4}{3}} \cdot x^{\frac{2}{3}} \cdot y^{\frac{5}{3}} \cdot z^{\frac{7}{3}} = 2yz^2\sqrt[3]{2x^2y^2z}$

6. $\sqrt{20x^7} = \left(2^2 \cdot 5 \cdot x^7\right)^{\frac{1}{2}} = 2^{\frac{2}{2}} \cdot 5^{\frac{1}{2}} \cdot x^{\frac{7}{2}} = 2x^3\sqrt{5x}$

7. $\sqrt{\dfrac{1}{3}} = \dfrac{\sqrt{1}}{\sqrt{3}} = \dfrac{\sqrt{1 \cdot 3}}{\sqrt{3 \cdot 3}} = \dfrac{\sqrt{3}}{3}$

8. $\sqrt{\dfrac{3}{8}} = \sqrt{\dfrac{3 \cdot 8}{8 \cdot 8}} = \dfrac{\sqrt{24}}{8} = \dfrac{\sqrt{2 \cdot 2 \cdot 6}}{8} = \dfrac{2\sqrt{6}}{8} = \dfrac{\sqrt{6}}{4}$

9. $\sqrt{\dfrac{3}{x}} = \sqrt{\dfrac{3 \cdot x}{x \cdot x}} = \dfrac{\sqrt{3x}}{x}$

10. $\sqrt[3]{\dfrac{3}{4}} = \sqrt[3]{\dfrac{3}{2 \cdot 2}} = \sqrt[3]{\dfrac{3 \cdot 2}{2 \cdot 2 \cdot 2}} = \dfrac{\sqrt[3]{6}}{2}$

Quiz 52

5. $\sqrt{8} = \sqrt{2 \cdot 2 \cdot 2} = 2\sqrt{2}$

6. $\sqrt{45} = \sqrt{3 \cdot 3 \cdot 5} = 3\sqrt{5}$

7. $\sqrt{50} = \sqrt{2 \cdot 5 \cdot 5} = 5\sqrt{2}$

8. $\sqrt[3]{81} = \sqrt[3]{3 \cdot 3 \cdot 3 \cdot 3} = 3\sqrt[3]{3}$

9. $\sqrt{2} = 2^{\frac{1}{2}} = 2^{\frac{2}{4}} = \sqrt[4]{2^2} = \sqrt[4]{4}$

11. $\sqrt{5} = 5^{\frac{1}{2}} = 5^{\frac{3}{6}} = \sqrt[6]{5^3} = \sqrt[6]{125}$

12. $\sqrt[3]{6} = 6^{\frac{1}{3}} = 6^{\frac{2}{6}} = \sqrt[6]{6^2} = \sqrt[6]{36}$

Quiz 53

5. $\sqrt{50} = \sqrt{2 \cdot 5 \cdot 5} = 5\sqrt{2}$

6. $\sqrt{\dfrac{1}{2}} = \sqrt{\dfrac{1 \cdot 2}{2 \cdot 2}} = \dfrac{\sqrt{2}}{2}$

7. $2\sqrt{8} = 2\sqrt{2 \cdot 2 \cdot 2} = 2 \cdot 2\sqrt{2} = 4\sqrt{2}$

9. $\sqrt{98} + \sqrt{72} = \sqrt{2 \cdot 7 \cdot 7} + \sqrt{2 \cdot 6 \cdot 6} = 7\sqrt{2} + 6\sqrt{2} = 13\sqrt{2}$

12. $4\sqrt{2} \cdot 3\sqrt{8} = 12\sqrt{16} = 12 \cdot 4 = 48$

Quiz 54

10. $y = x^2 - 4x + 3$

$x = \dfrac{-b}{2a}$

$x = \dfrac{-(-4)}{2(1)}$

$x = \dfrac{4}{2}$

$x = 2$

$y = x^2 - 4x + 3$

$y = 2^2 - 4(2) + 3$

$y = 4 - 8 + 3$

$y = -1$

$(2, -1)$

11. $y = 2x^2 - 8x + 6$

$x = \dfrac{-b}{2a}$

$x = \dfrac{-(-8)}{2(2)}$

$x = \dfrac{8}{4}$

$x = 2$

$y = 2x^2 - 8x + 6$

$y = 2(2^2) - 8(2) + 6$

$y = 2(4) - 16 + 6$

$y = 8 - 16 + 6$

$y = -2$

$(2, -2)$

Quiz 55

4. $x^2 = 12$

$x = \pm\sqrt{12}$

$x = \pm\sqrt{2 \cdot 2 \cdot 3}$

$x = \pm 2\sqrt{3}$

6. $x^2 = 18$

$x = \pm\sqrt{18}$

$x = \pm\sqrt{2 \cdot 3 \cdot 3}$

$x = \pm 3\sqrt{2}$

7. $x^2 = 56$

$x = \pm\sqrt{56}$

$x = \pm\sqrt{2 \cdot 2 \cdot 2 \cdot 7}$

$x = \pm 2\sqrt{14}$

8. $x^2 = 28$

$x = \pm\sqrt{28}$

$x = \pm\sqrt{2 \cdot 2 \cdot 7}$

$x = \pm 2\sqrt{7}$

9. $5x^2 = 100$

$x^2 = 20$

$x = \pm\sqrt{20}$

$x = \pm\sqrt{2 \cdot 2 \cdot 5}$

$x = \pm 2\sqrt{5}$

10. $3x^2 = 6$

$x^2 = 2$

$x = \pm\sqrt{2}$

Quiz 56

1. $x^2 + 10x + \underline{25}$

$\left(\frac{10}{2}\right)^2 = 5^2$

2. $x^2 - 30x + \underline{225}$

$\left(\frac{-30}{2}\right)^2 = (-15)^2$

3. $x^2 - 3x + \underline{\frac{9}{4}}$

$\left(\frac{-3}{2}\right)^2 = \frac{9}{4}$

4. $x^2 + 9x + \underline{\frac{81}{4}}$

$\left(\frac{9}{2}\right)^2 = \frac{81}{4}$

5–6. $x^2 - 6x = 7$

$x^2 - 6x + \left(\frac{-6}{2}\right)^2 = 7 + \left(\frac{-6}{2}\right)^2$

$x^2 - 6x + 9 = 7 + 9$

$(x - 3)^2 = 16$

$x - 3 = \pm 4$

$x = 3 + 4 = \mathbf{7}$

$x = 3 - 4 = \mathbf{-1}$

7–8. $x^2 + 10x = 11$

$x^2 + 10x + \left(\frac{10}{2}\right)^2 = 11 + \left(\frac{10}{2}\right)^2$

$x^2 + 10x + 25 = 11 + 25$

$(x + 5)^2 = 36$

$x + 5 = \pm 6$

$x = -5 + 6 = \mathbf{1}$

$x = -5 - 6 = \mathbf{-11}$

9–10. $x^2 - 5x + 2 = 0$

$x^2 - 5x = -2$

$x^2 - 5x + \left(\frac{-5}{2}\right)^2 = -2 + \left(\frac{-5}{2}\right)^2$

$x^2 - 5x + \frac{25}{4} = -2 + \frac{25}{4}$

$\left(x - \frac{5}{2}\right)^2 = \frac{-2(4)}{4} + \frac{25}{4}$

$\left(x - \frac{5}{2}\right)^2 = \frac{-8 + 25}{4}$

$\left(x - \frac{5}{2}\right)^2 = \frac{17}{4}$

$x - \frac{5}{2} = \frac{\pm\sqrt{17}}{2}$

$x = \mathbf{\dfrac{5 + \sqrt{17}}{2}} \; ; \; x = \mathbf{\dfrac{5 - \sqrt{17}}{2}}$

Quiz 57

8–9. $x^2 - 6x = -5$

$x^2 - 6x + 5 = 0$

$x = \dfrac{6 \pm \sqrt{36 - 4(1)(5)}}{2}$

$x = \dfrac{6 \pm \sqrt{16}}{2}$

$x = \dfrac{6 \pm 4}{2}$

$x = \dfrac{6 + 4}{2} = \dfrac{10}{2} = \mathbf{5}$

$x = \dfrac{6 - 4}{2} = \dfrac{2}{2} = \mathbf{1}$

10–11. $x^2 - x = 4$

$x^2 - x - 4 = 0$

$x = \dfrac{1 \pm \sqrt{1 - 4(1)(-4)}}{2}$

$x = \dfrac{1 \pm \sqrt{17}}{2}$

$x = \mathbf{\dfrac{1 + \sqrt{17}}{2}}$

$x = \dfrac{1 - \sqrt{17}}{2}$

183

Test Solution Key

Test 1

9. $\dfrac{3x}{3} = \dfrac{15}{3}$

$\qquad x = 5$

10. $6a + 2a - 1 = 15$

$\qquad 8a - 1 = 15$

$\qquad 8a - 1 + 1 = 15 + 1$

$\qquad \dfrac{8a}{8} = \dfrac{16}{8}$

$\qquad a = 2$

11. $(2)\dfrac{x}{2} = 3(2)$

$\qquad x = 6$

12. $\qquad x - 3 = 6$

$\qquad x - 3 + 3 = 6 + 3$

$\qquad x = 9$

13. $\dfrac{1.5n}{1.5} = \dfrac{3.0}{1.5}$

$\qquad n = 2$

14. $\qquad 2m + 5 = 25$

$\qquad 2m + 5 - 5 = 25 - 5$

$\qquad 2m = 20$

$\qquad m = 10$

15. $2\frac{1}{2}x = 10$

$\qquad \dfrac{5}{2}x = 10$

$\qquad (2)\dfrac{5}{2}x = 10(2)$

$\qquad 5x = 20$

$\qquad x = 4$

16. $3n + 7 - 2 = 8$

$\qquad 3n + 5 = 8$

$\qquad 3n + 5 - 5 = 8 - 5$

$\qquad \dfrac{3n}{3} = \dfrac{3}{3}$

$\qquad n = 1$

17. $3a + 2a - a$

$\quad = 5a - a$

$\quad = 4a$

18. $2b + 3c - b - b + c$

$\quad = 2b - b - b + 3c + c$

$\quad = 2b - 2b + 3c + c$

$\quad = 4c$

19. $3x + 2y + 5x - y$

$\quad = 3x + 5x + 2y - y$

$\quad = 8x + y$

20. $4(5)(2)$

$\quad = (20)(2)$

$\quad 40$

21. $\dfrac{3 \cdot 4}{2} = \dfrac{12}{2} = 6$

22. $3(4)(3) - (3)(2)$

$\quad = (12)(3) - (3)(2)$

$\quad = 36 - 6$

$\quad = 30$

23. Let $x = $ 1st number $\quad$ (8)

$\qquad 3x = $ 2nd number $\quad$ (24)

$\qquad 3x + x = 32$

$\qquad \dfrac{4x}{4} = \dfrac{32}{4}$

$\qquad x = 8$

Substitute $3(8) = 24$

24. Let $x = $ 1st number (9)

$\qquad 2x - \frac{1}{3}x = 15$

$\qquad \frac{6}{3}x - \frac{1}{3}x = 15$

$\qquad (3)\frac{5}{3}x = 15(3)$

$\qquad 5x = 45$

$\qquad x = 9$

25. Let $x = $ 1st part $\quad$ (14)

$\qquad 2x = $ 2nd part (28)

$\qquad 4x = $ 3rd part (56)

$\qquad x + 2x + 4x = 98$

$\qquad \dfrac{7x}{7} = \dfrac{98}{7}$

$\qquad x = 14$

$\qquad 2x = 28$

$\qquad 4(14) = 56$

Test 2

1. Trinomial

2. Pie graph

5. One

6.   Let x = 1st part (69)

       $\frac{1}{3}x$ = 2nd part (23)

    $x + \frac{1}{3}x = 92$

    $\frac{3}{3}x + \frac{1}{3}x = 92$

    $(3)\frac{4}{3}x = 92(3)$

        $4x = 276$

         $x = 69$

    $\left(\frac{1}{3}\right)(69) = 23$

7.   Let d = distance traveled in morning

      $3d$ = distance traveled in afternoon

   $d + 3d = 420$

    $\frac{4d}{4} = \frac{420}{4}$

     $d = 105$ miles

8.   Let x = number of girls (18)

   $2x - 12$ = number of boys (24)

  $x + 2x - 12 = 42$

     $3x - 12 = 42$

  $3x - 12 + 12 = 42 + 12$

       $\frac{3x}{3} = \frac{54}{3}$

         $x = 18$

  $2(18) - 12 = 24$

13. $(3)(2)^3$

  $= (3)(8)$

  $= 24$

14. $(2 + 4)^2$

  $= 6^2$

  $= 36$

15. $\dfrac{4^2}{4(2)} + \dfrac{0(3)}{7(4)}$

  $= \dfrac{16}{4(2)} + \dfrac{0(3)}{7(4)}$

  $= \dfrac{16}{8} + \dfrac{0}{28}$

  $= 2 + 0$

  $= 2$

16. $4 + (3)(2) - 4 \div 2$

  $= 4 + 6 - 4 \div 2$

  $= 4 + 6 - 2$

  $= 10 - 2$

  $= 8$

17. $(4 - 1)(3 + 2)$

  $= (3)(5)$

  $= 15$

18. $5a^2 + a + 4 + 3a - 2a^2 - 3 - 2a$

  $= 5a^2 - 2a^2 + 3a + a - 2a + 4 - 3$

  $= 3a^2 + 2a + 1$

19. $7a + b + 5b - 2a - 3b + 4a$

  $= 7a - 2a + 4a + 5b + b - 3b$

  $= 9a + 3b$

20. $3x^2 + x + 6 - x^2 + 5x - 4 + 2x^2 - 2x + 2$

  $= 3x^2 + 2x^2 - x^2 + 5x - 2x + x - 4 + 6 + 2$

  $= 4x^2 + 4x + 4$

21. $8mn + 10 - 6mn + 2mn - 5 - 2 + 8$

  $= 8mn - 6mn + 2mn + 10 - 5 - 2 + 8$

  $= 4mn + 11$

22. $i = prt$

  $\dfrac{i}{pt} = \dfrac{(pt)r}{(pt)}$

  $\dfrac{i}{pt} = r$

Test Solutions

Test 2 continued

23. $\dfrac{C}{2\pi} = \dfrac{2\pi r}{2\pi}$

$\dfrac{C}{2\pi} = r$

24.

$P = 2a + 2b$ ***or***

$\dfrac{P}{2} = \dfrac{2(a + b)}{2}$

$\dfrac{P}{2} = a + b$

$\dfrac{P}{2} - a = a - a + b$

$\dfrac{P}{2} - a = b$

$P = 2a + 2b$

$P - 2a = 2a + 2b - 2a$

$\dfrac{P - 2a}{2} = \dfrac{2b}{2}$

$\dfrac{P - 2a}{2} = b$

25. $\dfrac{A}{(b + b')} = \dfrac{\frac{1}{2}h(b + b')}{(b + b')}$

$(2)\dfrac{A}{b + b'} = \frac{1}{2}h(2)$

$\dfrac{2A}{b + b'} = h$

26. $A = (6\text{ in.})(4\text{ in.})$

$A = 24$ sq. in.

27. $A = \frac{1}{2}(6)(12 + 8)$

$A = \frac{1}{2}(6)(20)$

$A = (3)(20)$

$A = 60$ sq. in.

28. $C = \frac{5}{9}(68° - 32°)$

$C = \frac{5}{9}(36°)$

$C = \frac{5}{9}(9 \cdot 4)$

$C = 5(4)$

$C = 20°$

29. $\dfrac{V}{wh} = \dfrac{lwh}{wh}$

$\dfrac{V}{wh} = l$

$\dfrac{70}{(7)(2)} = l$

$\dfrac{70}{14} = l$

$5 = l$

Test 3

23. $5x - (7x + 7y)$

$= 5x - 7x - 7y$

$= -2x - 7y$

24. $(2a + 3b - 4c) + (a - 3b - 4c)$

$= 2a + 3b - 4c + a - 3b - 4c$

$= 3a - 8c$

25. $(2x^2 - 4xy + y^2) - (x^2 + 2xy - 3y^2)$

$= 2x^2 - 4xy + y^2 - x^2 - 2xy + 3y^2$

$= x^2 - 6xy + 4y^2$

26. $y - [5 - 3b - (7y - 4a)]$

$= y - [5 - 3b - 7y + 4a]$

$= y - 5 + 3b + 7y - 4a$

$= -4a + 3b + 8y - 5$

27. $3x - 12 + 12 = 9 + 12$

$3x = 21$

$x = 7$

28. $\dfrac{2x}{3} = 12$

$(3)\dfrac{2x}{3} = 12(3)$

$2x = 36$

$\dfrac{2x}{2} = \dfrac{36}{2}$

$x = 18$

29. $13x + 4 = 5x + 12$

$13x - 5x = 12 - 4$

$8x = 8$

$\dfrac{8x}{8} = \dfrac{8}{8}$

$x = 1$

30. $46 + 3x - 60 = 5x - 10 - 4x$

$3x - 14 = x - 10$

$3x - x = -10 + 14$

$2x = 4$

$\dfrac{2x}{2} = \dfrac{4}{2}$

$x = 2$

31. $10x - 39 + 12x - 9x + 42 - 4x = 42 - 4x$

$9x + 3 = 42 - 4x$

$9x + 4x = 42 - 3$

$13x = 39$

$\dfrac{13x}{13} = \dfrac{39}{13}$

$x = 3$

32. $3ab - 4ab + 7ab - 6ab + 4ab - 3ab = ab$

33. $11(a - b) - 2(a - b) - 1(a - b) + 10(a - b)$

$= (11 - 2 - 1 + 10)(a - b)$

$= 18(a - b)$

34. $15r + 6s - 11t + r - 9s + t - 2s + 5r - 2t - r$

$= 15r + r + 5r - r + 6s - 9s - 2s - 11t + t - 2t$

$= 20r - 5s - 12t$

35. $(6x^2 + 4xy - 3y^2) - (6x^2 - 3xy + 4y^2)$

$= 6x^2 + 4xy - 3y^2 - 6x^2 + 3xy - 4y^2$

$= 7xy - 7y^2$

36. $(3ab + a^2 + b^2) - (a^2 + 4ab + b^2)$

$= 3ab + a^2 + b^2 - a^2 - 4ab - b^2$

$= -ab$

37. Let $x = $ 1st number (11)

$x + 1 = $ 2nd number (12)

$x + 2 = $ 3rd number (13)

$3x = x + 1 + x + 2 + 8$

$3x = 2x + 11$

$x = 11$

$11 + 1 = 12$

$11 + 2 = 13$

38. $\dfrac{1}{5}n + n = 12$

$\dfrac{1}{5}n + \dfrac{5}{5}n = 12$

$(5)\dfrac{6}{5}n = 12(5)$

$\dfrac{6n}{6} = \dfrac{60}{6}$

$n = 10$

Test 4

1. $25^0 = 1$

2. $a^5 \cdot a^2 = a^{5+2} = a^7$

4. $4 - \left(-2a\right) = 4 + 2a$

5. $2x\left(3x + 4\right) = 6x + 8$

$$6x^2 + 8x = 6x + 8$$

$$x\left(6x + 8\right) \neq 6x + 8$$

(not true unless $x = 1$)

11. $\left(4 \cdot -7\right)\left(x^2 \cdot x\right) = -28x^3$

12. $\left(-3 \cdot -9\right)\left(-x\right)\left(y^2 \cdot y\right)\left(z\right) = 27xy^3z$

13. $\left(xyz\right)\left(xy\right) + \left(xyz\right)\left(yz\right) + \left(xyz\right)\left(xz\right)$

$$= x^2y^2z + xy^2z^2 + x^2yz^2$$

14. $\left(-3x^2\right)\left(4x^3\right) + \left(-3x^2\right)\left(6x^2\right) + \left(-3x^2\right)\left(2x\right) + \left(-3x^2\right)\left(1\right)$

$$= -12x^5 - 18x^4 - 6x^3 - 3x^2$$

15. $\left(x + 4\right)\left(x + 6\right)$

$$= x^2 + 6x + 4x + 24$$

$$= x^2 + 10x + 24$$

16. $\left(x - 2\right)\left(x^3 - 4x^2 - 7x + 10\right)$

$$= x^4 - 4x^3 - 7x^2 + 10x - 2x^3 + 8x^2 + 14x - 20$$

$$= x^4 - 6x^3 + x^2 + 24x - 20$$

17. $\dfrac{-20a^4b^5y^2}{-4a^2b^2y^2} = 5a^2b^3$

18. $\dfrac{-36a^4y^2z^3}{9az} = -4a^3y^2z^2$

19. $\dfrac{24r^3s^2 + 30r^2s^2 - 42r^2s^3}{6r^2s^2}$

$$= \dfrac{24r^3s^2}{6r^2s^2} + \dfrac{30r^2s^2}{6r^2s^2} - \dfrac{42r^2s^3}{6r^2s^2}$$

$$= 4r + 5 - 7s$$

20. $\dfrac{36a^3b^4c^6 + 60a^2b^5c^7}{-12a^2b^4c^6}$

$$= \dfrac{36a^3b^4c^6}{-12a^2b^4c^6} + \dfrac{60a^2b^5c^7}{-12a^2b^4c^6}$$

$$= -3a - 5bc$$

21.
$$
\begin{array}{r}
3a^2 - 2a + 3 \\
a + 4 \overline{\smash{\big)}\ 3a^3 + 10a^2 - 5a + 12} \\
\underline{3a^3 + 12a^2} \\
-2a^2 - 5a \\
\underline{-2a^2 - 8a} \\
3a + 12 \\
\underline{3a + 12} \\
0
\end{array}
$$

25.
Let x = 1st number $\left(32\right)$

$x + 1$ = 2nd number $\left(33\right)$

$x + 2$ = 3rd number $\left(34\right)$

$x + x + 1 + x + 2 = 99$

$3x + 3 = 99$

$3x = 96$

$x = 32$

$32 + 1 = 33$

$32 + 2 = 34$

26.
Let x = 1st piece $\left(14''\right)$

$x + 8$ = 2nd piece $\left(22''\right)$

$x + x + 8 = 36$

$2x + 8 = 36$

$2x = 28$

$x = 14$

$14 + 8 = 22$

Test 5

4. $(3a - 7)(4a + 5)$

$= 12a^2 + 15a - 28a - 35$

$= 12a^2 - 13a - 35$

5. $(5x - 2y)(3x - 3y)$

$= 15x^2 - 15xy - 6xy + 6y^2$

$= 15x^2 - 21xy + 6y^2$

6. $(7z - a)(3z + 2a)$

$= 21z^2 + 14az - 3az - 2a^2$

$= 21z^2 + 11az - 2a^2$

7. $(3ab + 10c^2)(3ab - 10c^2)$

$= 9a^2b^2 - 30abc^2 + 30abc^2 - 100c^4$

$= 9a^2b^2 - 100c^4$

8. $(x + 5)(x + 6)$

$= x^2 + 5x + 6x + 30$

$= x^2 + 11x + 30$

9. $(x - 7)(x + 8)$

$= x^2 + 8x - 7x - 56$

$= x^2 + x - 56$

10. $(y + 3)(y + 3)$

$= y^2 + 3y + 3y + 9$

$= y^2 + 6y + 9$

11. $(4xy - 7)(4xy - 7)$

$= 16x^2y^2 - 28xy - 28xy + 49$

$= 16x^2y^2 - 56xy + 49$

12. $\left(y - \frac{1}{4}\right)\left(y - \frac{1}{4}\right)$

$= y^2 - \frac{1}{4}y - \frac{1}{4}y + \frac{1}{16}$

$= y^2 - \frac{1}{2}y + \frac{1}{16}$

13. $(3m + n)(3m - n)$

$= 9m^2 - 3mn + 3mn - n^2$

$= 9m^2 - n^2$

14. $(4r^2 - 3rt - t^2)(5r^2 - 2rt - 3t^2)$

$= 20r^4 - 8r^3t - 12r^2t^2 - 15r^3t + 6r^2t^2 + 9rt^3$
$\qquad\qquad\qquad\qquad - 5r^2t^2 + 2rt^3 + 3t^4$

$= 20r^4 - 23r^3t - 11r^2t^2 + 11rt^3 + 3t^4$

30. Let $2x = $ 1st number (36)

$2x + 2 = $ 2nd number (38)

$2x + 4 = $ 3rd number (40)

$2x + 6 = $ 4th number (42)

$2x + 2x + 2 + 2x + 4 + 2x + 6 = 156$

$8x + 12 = 156$

$8x = 144$

$x = 18$

$2(18) = 36$

$2(18) + 2 = 38$

$2(18) + 4 = 40$

$2(18) + 6 = 42$

31. Let $x = $ age of son (3)

$x + 28 = $ age of Mr. Jones (31)

$3(x + 11) = x + 28 + 11$

$3x + 33 = x + 39$

$2x = 6$

$x = 3$

$x + 28 = 31$

Test 6

1. $2x + 3x = 45$

$$\frac{5x}{5} = \frac{45}{5}$$

$$x = 9$$

2. $2x - 11 = 29$

$$\frac{2x}{2} = \frac{40}{2}$$

$$x = 20$$

3. $\dfrac{2x}{3} = 12$

$$(3)\frac{2x}{3} = 12(3)$$

$$2x = 36$$

$$x = 18$$

4. $6x + 2x - 1 = 15$

$$8x - 1 = 15$$

$$\frac{8x}{8} = \frac{16}{8}$$

$$x = 2$$

5. $5x - 6 = 50 - 2x$

$$\frac{7x}{7} = \frac{56}{7}$$

$$x = 8$$

6. $2(3x - 5) = 4x + 12$

$$6x - 10 = 4x + 12$$

$$2x = 22$$

$$x = 11$$

9.
$$\begin{array}{r} 8x - \ y \\ -(4x \ - 7y) \\ \hline \end{array} = \begin{array}{r} 8x - \ y \\ -4x + 7y \\ \hline 4x + 6y \end{array}$$

10.
$$\begin{array}{r} 15x - 3y + 2z \\ -(3x + 8y - 9z) \\ \hline \end{array} = \begin{array}{r} 15x - 3y + 2z \\ -3x - 8y + 9z \\ \hline -12x - 11y + 11z \end{array}$$

12. $(2x + 6)(3x + 2)$

$$= 6x^2 + 4x + 18x + 12$$

$$= 6x^2 + 22x + 12$$

13. $(5x - 2y)(3x - 3y)$

$$= 15x^2 - 15xy - 6xy + 6y^2$$

$$= 15x^2 - 21xy + 6y^2$$

14. $(4a - 2b)(3a + 3b)$

$$= 12a^2 + 12ab - 6ab - 6b^2$$

$$= 12a^2 + 6ab - 6b^2$$

15. $(a - 3b)^2$

$$= (a - 3b)(a - 3b)$$

$$= a^2 - 3ab - 3ab + 9b^2$$

$$= a^2 - 6ab + 9b^2$$

16. $\left(s - \frac{3}{5}\right)\left(s - \frac{3}{5}\right)$

$$= s^2 - \frac{3}{5}s - \frac{3}{5}s + \frac{9}{25}$$

$$= s^2 - \frac{6}{5}s + \frac{9}{25}$$

17. $(b^2 + 5b - 4)(2b^2 - 3b - 4)$

$$= 2b^4 - 3b^3 - 4b^2 + 10b^3 - 15b^2 - 20b - 8b^2 + 12b + 16$$

$$= 2b^4 + 7b^3 - 27b^2 - 8b + 16$$

19. $\dfrac{9x^2y^2 + 15xy^2}{-3xy} = \dfrac{9x^2y^2}{-3xy} + \dfrac{15xy^2}{-3xy} = -3xy - 5y$

20.
$$\require{enclose}\begin{array}{r} 3a^2 - 2a + 3 \\ a + 4 \enclose{longdiv}{3a^3 + 10a^2 - 5a + 12} \\ \underline{3a^3 + 12a^2} \\ -2a^2 - 5a \\ \underline{-2a^2 - 8a} \\ 3a + 12 \\ \underline{3a + 12} \\ 0 \end{array}$$

28. $3x^5 - 3x$

$$= 3x(x^4 - 1)$$

$$= 3x(x^2 + 1)(x^2 - 1)$$

$$= 3x(x^2 + 1)(x + 1)(x - 1)$$

Test 6 continued

29. $a^2 - (b - c)^2$

$= [a - (b - c)][a + (b - c)]$

$= (a - b + c)(a + b - c)$

30. $12x^2 + 2x - 24$

$= 2(6x^2 + x - 12)$

$= 2(2x + 3)(3x - 4)$

31. $x + \dfrac{1}{8}x = 54$

$(8)\dfrac{9}{8}x = 54(8)$

$9x = 432$

$x = 48$

32.

$\text{Let } 2x = \text{1st number} \quad (20)$

$2x + 2 = \text{2nd number} \quad (22)$

$2x + 4 = \text{3rd number} \quad (24)$

$2x + 2x + 4 + 22 = 3(2x + 2)$

$4x + 4 + 22 = 6x + 6$

$-2x + 26 = 6$

$\dfrac{-2x}{-2} = \dfrac{-20}{-2}$

$x = 10$

$2(10) = 20$

$2(10) + 2 = 22$

$2(10) + 4 = 24$

Test 7

4. $\dfrac{2x}{4x^2 - 6ax} = \dfrac{2x}{2x(2x - 3a)} = \dfrac{1}{2x - 3a}$

5. $\dfrac{x^2 - 6x - 7}{x^2 - 11x + 28} = \dfrac{(x - 7)(x + 1)}{(x - 4)(x - 7)} = \dfrac{x + 1}{x - 4}$

6. $\dfrac{4a + 7}{16a^2 - 49} = \dfrac{4a + 7}{(4a - 7)(4a + 7)} = \dfrac{1}{4a - 7}$

7. $\dfrac{36ac + 9c}{9c} = \dfrac{36ac}{9c} + \dfrac{9c}{9c} = 4a + 1$

8. $\dfrac{4x^3 - 8x^2 + 2x - 1}{2x} = \dfrac{4x^3}{2x} - \dfrac{8x^2}{2x} + \dfrac{2x}{2x} - \dfrac{1}{2x} = 2x^2 - 4x + 1 - \dfrac{1}{2x}$

9. $\dfrac{2x}{5} + \dfrac{3x}{2} = \dfrac{2(2x)}{10} + \dfrac{5(3x)}{10} = \dfrac{4x}{10} + \dfrac{15x}{10} = \dfrac{19x}{10}$

10. $\dfrac{4m}{3} - \dfrac{5m}{6} = \dfrac{2(4m)}{6} - \dfrac{5m}{6} = \dfrac{8m - 5m}{6} = \dfrac{3m}{6} = \dfrac{m}{2}$

11. $\dfrac{2x + 1}{3} + \dfrac{x - 2}{4} - \dfrac{x - 3}{6} + \dfrac{5 - x}{2}$

$= \dfrac{4(2x + 1)}{12} + \dfrac{3(x - 2)}{12} - \dfrac{2(x - 3)}{12} + \dfrac{6(5 - x)}{12}$

$= \dfrac{8x + 4 + 3x - 6 - 2x + 6 + 30 - 6x}{12}$

$= \dfrac{3x + 34}{12}$

Test 7 continued

12. $a + x - \dfrac{x^2}{a - x}$

$= \dfrac{a(a - x)}{a - x} + \dfrac{x(a - x)}{a - x} - \dfrac{x^2}{a - x}$

$= \dfrac{a^2 - ax + ax - x^2 - x^2}{a - x}$

$= \dfrac{a^2 - 2x^2}{a - x}$

13. $\dfrac{x}{x - 2} - \dfrac{x - 2}{x + 2}$

$= \dfrac{x(x + 2)}{(x - 2)(x + 2)} - \dfrac{(x - 2)(x - 2)}{(x - 2)(x + 2)}$

$= \dfrac{x^2 + 2x - (x^2 - 4x + 4)}{(x - 2)(x + 2)}$

$= \dfrac{x^2 + 2x - x^2 + 4x - 4}{(x - 2)(x + 2)}$

$= \dfrac{6x - 4}{(x - 2)(x + 2)}$

14. $\dfrac{12}{x - 3} + \dfrac{5}{x^2 - 5x + 6}$

$= \dfrac{12(x - 2)}{(x - 3)(x - 2)} + \dfrac{5}{(x - 3)(x - 2)}$

$= \dfrac{12x - 24 + 5}{(x - 3)(x - 2)}$

$= \dfrac{12x - 19}{(x - 3)(x - 2)}$

15. $\dfrac{3ab}{4xy} \cdot \dfrac{2y}{3a^2} = \dfrac{b}{2ax}$

16. $\dfrac{4mn}{3xy} \cdot \dfrac{15bx}{16m^2} = \dfrac{5bn}{4my}$

17. $\dfrac{a + c}{2} \cdot \dfrac{6}{a^2 - c^2} = \dfrac{a + c}{2} \cdot \dfrac{6}{(a + c)(a - c)} = \dfrac{3}{a - c}$

18. $\dfrac{x^2 + 2x + 1}{y} \cdot \dfrac{4y^2}{x^2 - 1}$

$= \dfrac{(x + 1)(x + 1)}{y} \cdot \dfrac{4y^2}{(x + 1)(x - 1)}$

$= \dfrac{4y(x + 1)}{x - 1}$ or $\dfrac{4xy + 4y}{x - 1}$

19. $\dfrac{x^2 + 3x + 2}{x^2 - 3x - 10} \cdot \dfrac{x^2 - 6x + 5}{x^2 + 8x + 7}$

$= \dfrac{(x + 2)(x + 1)}{(x - 5)(x + 2)} \cdot \dfrac{(x - 5)(x - 1)}{(x + 7)(x + 1)}$

$= \dfrac{x - 1}{x + 7}$

Test 8

1. $\dfrac{5mn}{6bx} \div \dfrac{10m^2n}{3ax^2} = \dfrac{5mn}{6bx} \cdot \dfrac{3ax^2}{10m^2n} = \dfrac{ax}{4bm}$

3. $\dfrac{\frac{4}{7}}{\frac{7}{m}} = \dfrac{4}{7} \cdot \dfrac{m}{7} = \dfrac{4m}{49}$

4. $\dfrac{\frac{2b}{3c}}{\frac{4b^2}{9c^2}} = \dfrac{2b}{3c} \cdot \dfrac{9c^2}{4b^2} = \dfrac{3c}{2b}$

5. $\qquad \dfrac{x}{2} + \dfrac{x}{6} = \dfrac{10}{3}$

$$(6)\dfrac{x}{2} + (6)\dfrac{x}{6} = \dfrac{10}{3}(6)$$

$$3x + x = 20$$

$$4x = 20$$

$$x = 5$$

6. $\qquad \dfrac{25x}{18} - \dfrac{5x}{9} + \dfrac{2x}{3} - \dfrac{5x}{6} = 2$

$$(18)\dfrac{25x}{18} - (18)\dfrac{5x}{9} + (18)\dfrac{2x}{3} - (18)\dfrac{5x}{6} = (18)2$$

$$25x - 10x + 12x - 15x = 36$$

$$12x = 36$$

$$x = 3$$

7. $\qquad \dfrac{3x}{4} + \dfrac{7x}{16} - \dfrac{x}{2} - \dfrac{9x}{16} = \dfrac{1}{8}$

$$(16)\dfrac{3x}{4} + (16)\dfrac{7x}{16} - (16)\dfrac{x}{2} - (16)\dfrac{9x}{16} = (16)\dfrac{1}{8}$$

$$12x + 7x - 8x - 9x = 2$$

$$2x = 2$$

$$x = 1$$

8. $\qquad \dfrac{m-2}{m+3} = \dfrac{3}{4}$

$$4(m-2) = 3(m+3) \quad \text{(cross multiplied)}$$

$$4m - 8 = 3m + 9$$

$$m = 17$$

Test 8 continued

9.

$$\frac{4}{x + 2} + \frac{7}{x + 3} = \frac{37}{(x + 2)(x + 3)}$$

$$(x + 2)(x + 3)\frac{4}{x + 2} + (x + 2)(x + 3)\frac{7}{x + 3} = \frac{37}{(x + 2)(x + 3)}(x + 2)(x + 3)$$

$$4(x + 3) + 7(x + 2) = 37$$

$$4x + 12 + 7x + 14 = 37$$

$$11x + 26 = 37$$

$$11x = 11$$

$$x = 1$$

10. $\dfrac{4m}{8m} = \dfrac{1}{2}$

11. $\dfrac{5}{9} = \dfrac{25}{45}$

$\dfrac{3}{5} = \dfrac{27}{45}$

$\dfrac{27}{45} > \dfrac{25}{45}$

$\dfrac{3}{5}$ is greater

12. $\dfrac{21}{7} = \dfrac{3}{1}$

13. $\dfrac{2}{3} = \dfrac{4}{x}$

$2x = 12$

$x = 6$

14. $\dfrac{10}{6} = \dfrac{x + 2}{x}$

$10x = 6(x + 2)$

$10x = 6x + 12$

$4x = 12$

$x = 3$

15. $\dfrac{3}{1} = \dfrac{x - 2}{x + 2}$

$3(x + 2) = 1(x - 2)$

$3x + 6 = x - 2$

$2x = -8$

$x = -4$

16. $\dfrac{7}{5} = \dfrac{210}{x}$

$7x = (5)(210)$

$7x = 1050$

$x = 150$ feet

17. $\dfrac{210}{p'} = \dfrac{2}{3}$

$3(210) = 2p'$

$630 = 2p'$

315 yards $= p'$

23. Let $x =$ smaller number (24)

$56 - x =$ larger number (32)

$\dfrac{3}{8}(56 - x) - 6 = \dfrac{1}{4}x$

$21 - \dfrac{3}{8}x - 6 = \dfrac{1}{4}x$

$168 - 3x - 48 = 2x$ (Multiply each term by 8.)

$-3x + 120 = 2x$

$-5x = -120$

$x = 24$

$56 - 24 = 32$

Test 9

1. $\dfrac{a-b}{2} - \dfrac{a+b}{3} = \dfrac{3(a-b)-2(a+b)}{6} = \dfrac{3a-3b-2a-2b}{6} = \dfrac{a-5b}{6}$

2. $\dfrac{b+c}{b^2-1} \cdot \dfrac{b+1}{b+c} = \dfrac{b+c}{(b-1)(b+1)} \cdot \dfrac{b+1}{b+c} = \dfrac{1}{b-1}$

3. $\dfrac{a-3}{a+7} \div \dfrac{a^2-9}{a^2+4a-21} = \dfrac{a-3}{a+7} \cdot \dfrac{a^2+4a-21}{a^2-9} = \dfrac{a-3}{a+7} \cdot \dfrac{(a+7)(a-3)}{(a+3)(a-3)} = \dfrac{a-3}{a+3}$

4.
$$\frac{x}{2} + \frac{x}{3} - \frac{x}{4} + \frac{3x}{10} - \frac{5x}{12} = 7$$

$$(60)\frac{x}{2} + (60)\frac{x}{3} - (60)\frac{x}{4} + (60)\frac{3x}{10} - (60)\frac{5x}{12} = 7(60)$$

$$30x + 20x - 15x + 18x - 25x = 420$$

$$28x = 420$$

$$x = 15$$

5. $\dfrac{x-2}{x+3} = \dfrac{3}{4}$

$4(x-2) = 3(x+3)$

$4x - 8 = 3x + 9$

$x = 17$

6. $\dfrac{5}{21} = \dfrac{x}{4200}$

$21x = (5)(4200)$

$21x = 21,000$

$x = 1000$ lb.

7. $\dfrac{V}{966} = \dfrac{1}{6}$

$V \cdot 6 = 966$

$V = 161$ cu. in.

8. $d = \frac{1}{2}gt^2$

$2d = gt^2$

$\dfrac{2d}{t^2} = g$

9. $\dfrac{V}{lh} = \dfrac{lwh}{lh}$

$\dfrac{V}{lh} = w$

16. $\begin{aligned} 7x - 5y &= 52 \\ +2x + 5y &= 47 \\ \hline 9x &= 99 \\ x &= 11 \end{aligned}$ $\qquad \begin{aligned} 7(11) - 5y &= 52 \\ 77 - 5y &= 52 \\ -5y &= -25 \\ y &= 5 \end{aligned}$

$(11, 5)$

17. $\begin{aligned} 6x - 5y &= 33 \\ +4x + 4y &= 44 \\ \hline \end{aligned}$ (multiply by 2) $\quad \begin{aligned} 12x - 10y &= 66 \\ -12x - 12y &= -132 \\ \hline -22y &= -66 \\ y &= 3 \end{aligned}$
 (multiply by -3)

Substitute: $12x - 10(3) = 66$

$12x - 30 = 66$

$12x = 96$

$x = 8$

$(8, 3)$

18. $x - y = 4$

$4y - x = 14$

Substitute $(4+y)$ for x in equation (2):

$4y - (4+y) = 14$

$4y - 4 - y = 14$

$3y - 4 = 14$

$3y = 18$

$y = 6$

Substitute: $x = 4 + 6$

$x = 10$

$(10, 6)$

Test 10

1. $\left(a^2 b^2 c^3\right)^2 = \left(a^2\right)^2 \cdot \left(b^2\right)^2 \cdot \left(c^3\right)^2 = a^4 b^4 c^6$

2. $\left(2a^2 c\right)^3 = 2^3 \cdot \left(a^2\right)^3 \cdot c^3 = 8a^6 c^3$

3. $\left(-2x^2 y\right)^3 = \left(-2\right)^3 \cdot \left(x^2\right)^3 \cdot y^3 = -8x^6 y^3$

4. $\left(-3x^3 y^2\right)^4 = \left(-3\right)^4 \cdot \left(x^3\right)^4 \cdot \left(y^2\right)^4 = 81x^{12} y^8$

5. $\left(-\dfrac{5}{ab}\right)^2 = \dfrac{\left(-5\right)\left(-5\right)}{\left(ab\right)\left(ab\right)} = \dfrac{25}{a^2 b^2}$

6. $\left(-\dfrac{3x}{2y}\right)^3 = \dfrac{\left(-3\right)^3 \cdot x^3}{2^3 \cdot y^3} = -\dfrac{27x^3}{8y^3}$

7. $\left(\dfrac{a^2 b^3}{xy^4}\right)^{2n} = \dfrac{\left(a^2\right)^{2n} \cdot \left(b^3\right)^{2n}}{x^{2n} \cdot \left(y^4\right)^{2n}} = \dfrac{a^{4n} b^{6n}}{x^{2n} y^{8n}}$

8. $\left(3x + 4y\right)^2$

   $= \left(3x + 4y\right)\left(3x + 4y\right)$

   $= 9x^2 + 12xy + 12xy + 16y^2$

   $= 9x^2 + 24xy + 16y^2$

9. $\left(a + b + c\right)^2$

   $= \left(a + b + c\right)\left(a + b + c\right)$

   $= a^2 + ab + ac + ab + b^2 + bc + ac + bc + c^2$

   $= a^2 + b^2 + c^2 + 2ab + 2ac + 2bc$

10. $\left(5a - 2c - 2b\right)^2$

    $= \left(5a - 2c - 2b\right)\left(5a - 2c - 2b\right)$

    $= 25a^2 - 10ac - 10ab - 10ac + 4c^2 + 4bc - 10ab + 4bc + 4b^2$

    $= 25a^2 + 4c^2 + 4b^2 - 20ac - 20ab + 8bc$

11. $\left(x + y\right)^3$

    $= \left(x + y\right)\left(x + y\right)\left(x + y\right)$

    $= \left(x + y\right)\left(x^2 + 2xy + y^2\right)$

    $= x^3 + 2x^2 y + xy^2 + x^2 y + 2xy^2 + y^3$

    $= x^3 + 3x^2 y + 3xy^2 + y^3$

12. $\sqrt[3]{a^3 b^6 c^9}$

    $= a^{\frac{3}{3}} b^{\frac{6}{3}} c^{\frac{9}{3}}$

    $= ab^2 c^3$

13. $\sqrt[5]{a^{10} x^5 y^{15}}$

    $= a^{\frac{10}{5}} x^{\frac{5}{5}} y^{\frac{15}{5}}$

    $= a^2 xy^3$

14. $\sqrt[3]{-8a^6 b^{15}}$

    $= -8^{\frac{1}{3}} a^{\frac{6}{3}} b^{\frac{15}{3}}$

    $= -2a^2 b^5$

15. $-\sqrt[3]{-27p^7 r^3}$

    $= -\left(-27^{\frac{1}{3}} p^{\frac{9}{3}} r^{\frac{3}{3}}\right)$

    $= -\left(-3p^3 r\right)$

    $= 3p^3 r$

Test 10 continued

16. $\sqrt[3]{\dfrac{-8x^9b^6}{27m^3n^{12}}}$

$= \dfrac{-8^{\frac{1}{3}}x^{\frac{9}{3}}b^{\frac{6}{3}}}{27^{\frac{1}{3}}m^{\frac{8}{3}}n^{\frac{12}{3}}}$

$= \dfrac{-2x^3b^2}{3mn^4}$

17.

$$c^2 - 12c + 36 \quad \underline{|c - 6}$$

	c^2
$2c$	$-12c + 36$
$2c - 6$	$-12c + 36$

18.

$$\dfrac{4a^2}{b^2} + 8 + \dfrac{4b^2}{a^2} \quad \underline{\Big|\dfrac{2a}{b} + \dfrac{2b}{a}}$$

$$\dfrac{4a^2}{b^2}$$

$\dfrac{4a}{b}$ $\qquad\qquad 8 + \dfrac{4b^2}{a^2}$

$\dfrac{4a}{b} + \dfrac{2b}{a}$ $\qquad 8 + \dfrac{4b^2}{a^2}$

19.

$$x^2 + 4xy + 4y^2 + 6xz + 12yz + 9z^2 \quad \underline{|x + 2y + 3z}$$

$\qquad\qquad x^2$

$2x \qquad\qquad 4xy + 4y^2 + 6xz + 12yz + 9z^2$

$2x + 2y \qquad\; 4xy + 4y^2$

$2x + 4y \qquad\qquad\quad 6xz + 12yz + 9z^2$

$2x + 4y + 3z \qquad\quad 6xz + 12yz + 9z^2$

20.

$$\begin{cases} ax + by = m \\ bx - ay = c \end{cases} \qquad\qquad \begin{cases} ax + by = m \\ bx - ay = c \end{cases}$$

$$\begin{cases} a^2x + aby = am \\ b^2x - aby = bc \end{cases} \qquad \begin{cases} abx + b^2y = bm \\ abx - a^2y = ac \end{cases}$$

$$\left(a^2 + b^2\right)x = am + bc \qquad \left(a^2 + b^2\right)y = bm - ac$$

$$x = \dfrac{am + bc}{a^2 + b^2} \qquad\qquad y = \dfrac{bm - ac}{a^2 + b^2}$$

Test 10 continued

21. Let x = number of \$1 bills
Let y = number of \$5 bills
$$\begin{cases} x + 5y = 86 \\ x + y = 38 \quad y = 38 - x \end{cases}$$

Substitute in first equation:
$$x + 5(38 - x) = 86$$

Solve: $\quad x + 5(38 - x) = 86$
$$x + 190 - 5x = 86$$
$$190 - 4x = 86$$
$$-4x = -104$$
$$x = 26$$
$$x + y = 38$$
$$26 + y = 38$$
$$y = 12$$
$\therefore$ number of \$1 bills = 26
number of \$5 bills = 12

22. Let x = number of adult tickets sold
Let y = number of student tickets sold
$$\begin{cases} 2.50x + 1.50y = 650 \\ x + y = 300 \quad y = 300 - x \end{cases}$$

Substitute in first equation
$$2.50x + 1.50(300 - x) = 650$$

Solve: $\quad 2.50x + 1.50(300 - x) = 650$
$$2.5x + 450 - 1.5x = 650$$
$$x + 450 = 650$$
$$x = 200$$
$$x + y = 300$$
$$200 + y = 300$$
$$y = 100$$
$\therefore$ number of adult tickets = 200
number of student tickets = 100

Test 11

10. $5\sqrt{x^{-1}y^{-1}}$
$= 5x^{-\frac{1}{2}}y^{-\frac{1}{2}}$
$= \dfrac{5}{x^{\frac{1}{2}}y^{\frac{1}{2}}}$

14. $a^3 \cdot a^{-2}$
$= a^{3+(-2)}$
$= a^1$
$= a$

15. $a^4 \cdot a^{-4}$
$= a^{4+(-4)}$
$= a^0$
$= 1$

16. $x^{\frac{1}{2}} \cdot x^{\frac{5}{2}}$
$= x^{\frac{1}{2}+\frac{5}{2}}$
$= x^{\frac{6}{2}}$
$= x^3$

17. $a^5 \div a^7$
$= a^{5-7}$
$= a^{-2}$

18. $a^2 \div a^{-1}$
$= a^{2-(-1)}$
$= a^3$

19. $x^{\frac{3}{2}} \div x^{-\frac{1}{2}}$
$= x^{\frac{3}{2}-\left(-\frac{1}{2}\right)}$
$= x^{\frac{4}{2}}$
$= x^2$

20. $x^{\frac{1}{2}} = 8$
$\left(x^{\frac{1}{2}}\right)^2 = 8^2$
$x = 64$

21. $x^{\frac{4}{3}} = 81$
$\left(x^{\frac{4}{3}}\right)^{\frac{3}{4}} = 81^{\frac{3}{4}}$
$x = 27$

22. $\sqrt{12}$
$= \sqrt{2 \cdot 2 \cdot 3}$
$= 2\sqrt{3}$

23. $4\sqrt{175}$
$= 4\sqrt{5 \cdot 5 \cdot 7}$
$= 4 \cdot 5\sqrt{7}$
$= 20\sqrt{7}$

24. $\sqrt{20a^5b^3}$
$= \sqrt{2^2 \cdot 5 \cdot a^5 \cdot b^3}$
$= 2^{\frac{2}{2}} \cdot 5^{\frac{1}{2}} \cdot a^{\frac{5}{2}} \cdot b^{\frac{3}{2}}$
$= 2a^2b\sqrt{5ab}$

Test 11 continued

25. $\sqrt{\frac{2}{3}} = \sqrt{\frac{2}{3} \cdot \frac{3}{3}} = \frac{\sqrt{6}}{3}$

26. $\sqrt{\frac{a}{2y^3}} = \sqrt{\frac{a \cdot 2y^3}{2y^3 \cdot 2y^3}} = \frac{\sqrt{2ay^3}}{2y^3} = \frac{y\sqrt{2ay}}{2y^3} = \frac{\sqrt{2ay}}{2y^2}$

27. $\sqrt[4]{25} = 25^{\frac{1}{4}} = \left(5^2\right)^{\frac{1}{4}} = 5^{\frac{2}{4}} = 5^{\frac{1}{2}} = \sqrt{5}$

28. $\sqrt[4]{121a^6x^4}$

$= 121^{\frac{1}{4}} \cdot a^{\frac{6}{4}} \cdot x^{\frac{4}{4}}$

$= \left(11^2\right)^{\frac{1}{4}} \cdot a^{\frac{4}{4}+\frac{2}{4}} \cdot x$

$= 11^{\frac{2}{4}} \cdot a^{\frac{4}{4}} \cdot a^{\frac{1}{2}} \cdot x$

$= 11^{\frac{1}{2}} \cdot a \cdot a^{\frac{1}{2}} \cdot x$

$= ax\sqrt{11a}$

29. $\sqrt{12} + 3\sqrt{75} - 2\sqrt{27}$

$= \sqrt{2^2 \cdot 3} + 3\sqrt{5^2 \cdot 3} - 2\sqrt{3^2 \cdot 3}$

$= 2\sqrt{3} + 3 \cdot 5\sqrt{3} - 2 \cdot 3\sqrt{3}$

$= 2\sqrt{3} + 15\sqrt{3} - 6\sqrt{3}$

$= \left(2 + 15 - 6\right)\sqrt{3}$

$= 11\sqrt{3}$

30. $\sqrt{3} \cdot \sqrt{15}$

$= \sqrt{3 \cdot 15}$

$= \sqrt{3 \cdot 3 \cdot 5}$

$= 3\sqrt{5}$

31. $\left(\sqrt{6} - \sqrt{5}\right)\left(\sqrt{6} - \sqrt{5}\right)$

$= 6 - \sqrt{30} - \sqrt{30} + 5$

$= 11 - 2\sqrt{30}$

33. $\frac{\sqrt{72}}{2\sqrt{6}} = \frac{1}{2}\sqrt{\frac{72}{6}} = \frac{1}{2}\sqrt{12} = \frac{1}{2}\left(2\sqrt{3}\right) = \sqrt{3}$

34. $\left(3\sqrt[6]{x^5}\right)^2 = \left(3x^{\frac{5}{6}}\right)^2 = 3^2 \cdot x^{\frac{10}{6}} = 9x^{\frac{5}{3}} = 9x^{\frac{3}{3}+\frac{2}{3}} = 9x\sqrt[3]{x^2}$

35. $\left(2\sqrt{ax^5}\right)^3 = \left(2a^{\frac{1}{2}}x^{\frac{5}{2}}\right)^3 = 2^3 a^{\frac{3}{2}}x^{\frac{15}{2}} = 8a^{\frac{2}{2}+\frac{1}{2}}x^{\frac{14}{2}+\frac{1}{2}} = 8ax^7\sqrt{ax}$

Test 12

2. $\sqrt{x^{16}} = x^8$

3. $\left(x^2 y^4 z\right)^0 = 1$

6. $a^5 \div a^8 = a^{-3}$

8. $\left(a+b\right)^2 = a^2 + 2ab + b^2$

9. $\sqrt{16x^4 y^2} = 4x^2 y$

11. $x^{\frac{5}{3}} = \sqrt[3]{x^5}$

13. The reciprocal of a is $\frac{1}{a}$.

16. $3x^{-1} = \frac{3}{x}$

19. $\sqrt{\frac{3}{5}} = \frac{\sqrt{15}}{5}$

20. $x = 27$

21.
$$x^2 + x = 12$$
$$x^2 + x - 12 = 0$$
$$\left(x+4\right)\left(x-3\right) = 0$$
$$x = -4; \quad x = 3$$

22.
$$x^2 + x - 6 = 0$$
$$\left(x+3\right)\left(x-2\right) = 0$$
$$x = -3; \quad x = 2$$

23.
$$2x^2 - x - 3 = 0$$
$$\left(2x-3\right)\left(x+1\right) = 0$$
$$x = \frac{3}{2}; \quad x = -1$$

25. $\left(\frac{10}{2}\right)^2 = 5^2 = 25$

26. $\left(\frac{3}{2}\right)^2 = \frac{9}{4}$

27. $\left(7 + \sqrt{3}\right)\left(7 - \sqrt{3}\right)$
$$= 49 - 7\sqrt{3} + 7\sqrt{3} - 3$$
$$= 46$$

28. $6\sqrt{2} + 5\sqrt{2} + \sqrt{2}$
$$= \left(6 + 5 + 1\right)\sqrt{2}$$
$$= 12\sqrt{2}$$

29. $\sqrt{8} + \sqrt{98} - \sqrt{72}$
$$= \sqrt{2^2 \cdot 2} + \sqrt{7^2 \cdot 2} - \sqrt{6^2 \cdot 2}$$
$$= 2\sqrt{2} + 7\sqrt{2} - 6\sqrt{2}$$
$$= \left(2 + 7 - 6\right)\sqrt{2}$$
$$= 3\sqrt{2}$$

30. $\left(\sqrt{7} - \sqrt{2}\right)\left(\sqrt{7} - \sqrt{2}\right)$
$$= \sqrt{49} - 2\sqrt{14} + \sqrt{4}$$
$$= 7 - 2\sqrt{14} + 2$$
$$= 9 - 2\sqrt{14}$$

31. $\begin{cases} 2x + 3y = 7 \\ x + y = 3 \end{cases}$
$$y = 3 - x$$
$$2x + 3\left(3 - x\right) = 7$$
$$2x + 9 - 3x = 7$$
$$-x = -2$$
$$x = 2$$
$$x + y = 3$$
$$2 + y = 3$$
$$y = 1$$

32. $\begin{cases} 3x - 4y = 26 \\ x - 8y = 22 \end{cases}$
$$x = 8y + 22$$
$$3\left(8y + 22\right) - 4y = 26$$
$$24y + 66 - 4y = 26$$
$$20y = -40$$
$$y = -2$$
$$x - 8y = 22$$
$$x - 8\left(-2\right) = 22$$
$$x + 16 = 22$$
$$x = 6$$

33. $\sqrt{40x^3}$
$$= \sqrt{2^2 \cdot 10 \cdot x^2 \cdot x}$$
$$= 2x\sqrt{10x}$$

Test 12 continued

34. $\sqrt{36x^3y^2}$

$= \sqrt{6^2 \cdot x^2 \cdot x \cdot y^2}$

$= 6xy\sqrt{x}$

35. $\sqrt{\dfrac{7}{3}} = \sqrt{\dfrac{7 \cdot 3}{3 \cdot 3}} = \dfrac{\sqrt{21}}{3}$

36. $\dfrac{x^2 - 1}{6} \cdot \dfrac{2}{x - 1}$

$= \dfrac{(x + 1)(x - 1)}{6} \cdot \dfrac{2}{x - 1}$

$= \dfrac{x + 1}{3}$

37. $\dfrac{x^2 - 10x + 21}{x^2 - 49} \div \dfrac{x - 3}{5}$

$= \dfrac{x^2 - 10x + 21}{x^2 - 49} \cdot \dfrac{5}{x - 3}$

$= \dfrac{(x - 7)(x - 3)}{(x - 7)(x + 7)} \cdot \dfrac{5}{x - 3}$

$= \dfrac{5}{x + 7}$

38. $(-3)^2 - 4(1)(2)$

$= 9 - 8$

$= 1$

39. $\left(3x^2 + 4xy - 5y^2\right) + \left(6x^2 - 8xy + 6y^2\right) - \left(2x^2 + 6xy + 9y^2\right)$

$= 3x^2 + 4xy - 5y^2 + 6x^2 - 8xy + 6y^2 - 2x^2 - 6xy - 9y^2$

$= 7x^2 - 10xy - 8y^2$

43. $(a + b - c)^2$

$= (a + b - c)(a + b - c)$

$= a^2 + ab - ac + ab + b^2 - bc - ac - bc + c^2$

$= a^2 + b^2 + c^2 + 2ab - 2ac - 2bc$

44. $\dfrac{2\sqrt{48}}{6\sqrt{8}}$

$= \dfrac{2}{6}\sqrt{\dfrac{48}{8}}$

$= \dfrac{1}{3}\sqrt{6}$

$= \dfrac{\sqrt{6}}{3}$

45. $\dfrac{5y - 1}{2y} + \dfrac{5y + 2}{3y}$

$= \dfrac{3(5y - 1)}{3(2y)} + \dfrac{2(5y + 2)}{2(3y)}$

$= \dfrac{15y - 3}{6y} + \dfrac{10y + 4}{6y}$

$= \dfrac{15y - 3 + 10y + 4}{6y}$

$= \dfrac{25y + 1}{6y}$

46. Let x = first number

Let y = second number

$\begin{cases} x + y = 71 \\ x - y = 13 \end{cases}$

$2x = 84$

$x = 42$

$x + y = 71$

$42 + y = 71$

$y = 29$

47. $y = x^2 - 4x + 3$

x-coordinate $= \dfrac{-b}{2a}$

$= \dfrac{-(-4)}{2(1)}$

$= \dfrac{4}{2}$

$= 2$

$y = x^2 - 4x + 3$

$= 2^2 - 4(2) + 3$

$= 4 - 8 + 3$

$= -1$